Northpoint Horizons™

Science
CAVS™
Content Academic Vocabulary System

A Comprehensive
Hands-On Research-Based
Science
Vocabulary System

Research + Hands-on System = Academic Success

Northpoint
Horizons™

*Dedicated to
the success of
the struggling
student.*

Are your students struggling to comprehend their science texts?

Are they failing the science assessments?

Research shows that **systematic, direct instruction** and **hands-on practice/reinforcement** of content vocabulary leads to success in comprehension.

Now, Northpoint Horizons™ brings you:

The Total Solution for Science Vocabulary Success!

✓ Research-Based and Field Tested

✓ Differentiated Instruction for All Levels

✓ Systematic, Direct Instruction

✓ Hands-On Learning for Practice and Reinforcement

✓ Focus on Content Vocabulary Assessed on State Tests

✓ Grades K–2 and Grades 3–5

Ensure Students' Success in Science

5 Easy Steps

 **STEP 1 Engage** — **Build Background** for Content Academic Vocabulary

 **STEP 2 Explore** — **Model** and Involve Students in Hands-On Learning Activity

 **STEP 3 Explain** — Provide **Systematic Instruction** for Content Academic Vocabulary

 **STEP 4 Elaborate** — Provide **Practice and Reinforcement** of Content Academic Vocabulary

 **STEP 5 Evaluate** — **Assess and Reinforce** Students' Learning

Science Academic Vocabulary Acquisition

Vocabulary Acquisition

o Success with

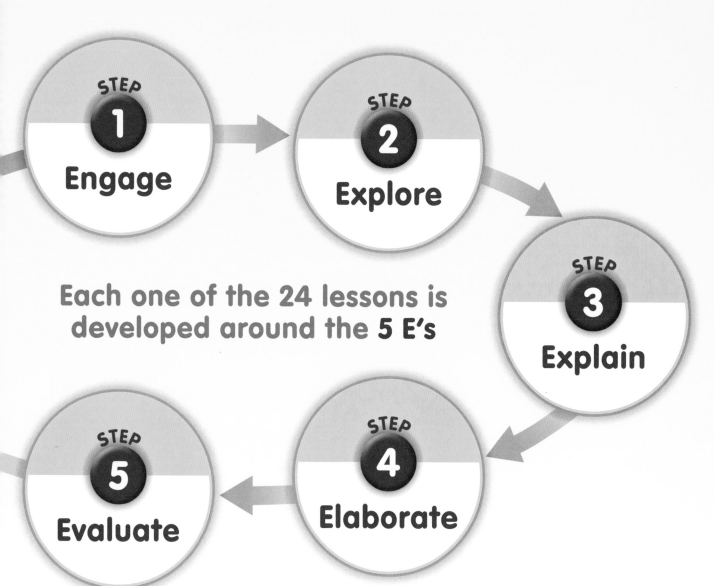

STEP 1 Engage

STEP 2 Explore

Each one of the 24 lessons is developed around the **5 E's**

STEP 3 Explain

STEP 5 Evaluate

STEP 4 Elaborate

Engage
Build Background

The teacher leads a discussion about the new vocabulary words using the students' experiences and descriptions in an oral language activity.

Vocabulary Cards
- 83 Cards for Grades K–2
- 110 Cards for Grades 3–5

Posters
- 8 Posters for Grades K–2
- 8 Posters for Grades 3–5

Concept Poster 6
Use with Lessons 17 and 18.

Lesson 17: What makes things move?
How does the boy's energy change as he goes down the slide?

Lesson 18: How do simple machines help things move?
What simple machines do you see here?

gravity

friction

potential energy

kinetic energy

The roller... has the m... **potentia**... at the top...

Potential energy changes to **kinetic energy** as the roller coaster moves down the track.

STEP 2

Explore & Learn

Modeling and Discussing Through Hands-On Learning

Students experience and understand vocabulary
and concepts through hands-on activities.

Manipulatives

Recording Sheet
USE WITH ACTIVITY 17

Name _____

Observe Friction

4 Record

Use the chart to show what you measured.

Kind of paper	How far box moved
wax paper	
sandpaper	

5 Share
• Tell why you got the results you did.

_____
_____
_____

Now Try This

Do the activity again, but put a wooden block in the box with the balloon.
Do you think the box will travel as far?

Prediction: _____

Results: _____

Activity Record Sheets
• 24 Record Sheets for Grades K–2
• 24 Record Sheets for Grades 3–5

Activity Placemats
• 72 Placemats for Grades K–2
• 72 Placemats for Grades 3–5

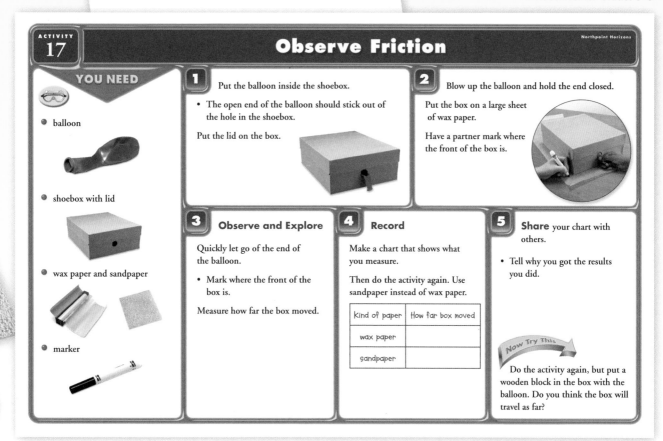

ACTIVITY 17

Observe Friction

Northpoint Horizons

YOU NEED
• balloon
• shoebox with lid
• wax paper and sandpaper
• marker

1
Put the balloon inside the shoebox.
• The open end of the balloon should stick out of the hole in the shoebox.
Put the lid on the box.

2
Blow up the balloon and hold the end closed.
Put the box on a large sheet of wax paper.
Have a partner mark where the front of the box is.

3 Observe and Explore
Quickly let go of the end of the balloon.
• Mark where the front of the box is.
Measure how far the box moved.

4 Record
Make a chart that shows what you measure.
Then do the activity again. Use sandpaper instead of wax paper.

Kind of paper	How far box moved
wax paper	
sandpaper	

5 Share your chart with others.
• Tell why you got the results you did.

Now Try This
Do the activity again, but put a wooden block in the box with the balloon. Do you think the box will travel as far?

⑨

STEP 3

Explain Concepts and

Provide Systematic, Direct Instruction

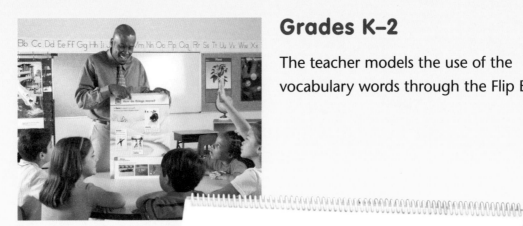

Grades K–2

The teacher models the use of the vocabulary words through the Flip Book.

Flip Book
- 1 Book, 24 pages for Grades K–2 only

Vocabulary

Grades 3–5

The teacher and students read and discuss the vocabulary words in context.

Reader Card A – for Beginning/Emerging learners

Reader Card B – for Intermediate/Expanding learners

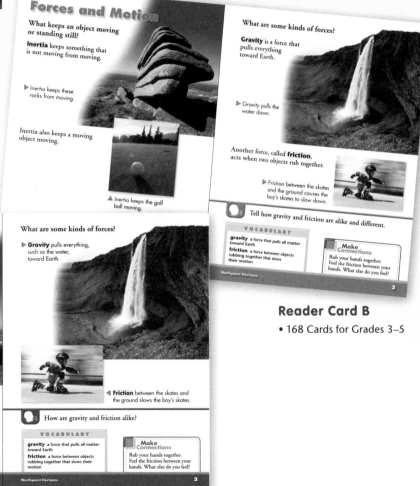

Reader Card A
• 168 Cards for Grades 3–5

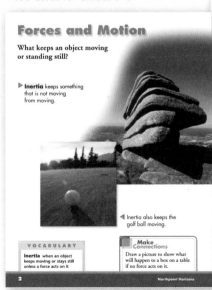

Reader Card B
• 168 Cards for Grades 3–5

STEP 4

Elaborate

Provide Practice and Reinforcement

Students practice vocabulary—listen, read, write, speak—with the Radius™ Audio Learning System.

Science Journal
• A set of 20 Journals

Hands-On Learning for Practice/Reinforcement

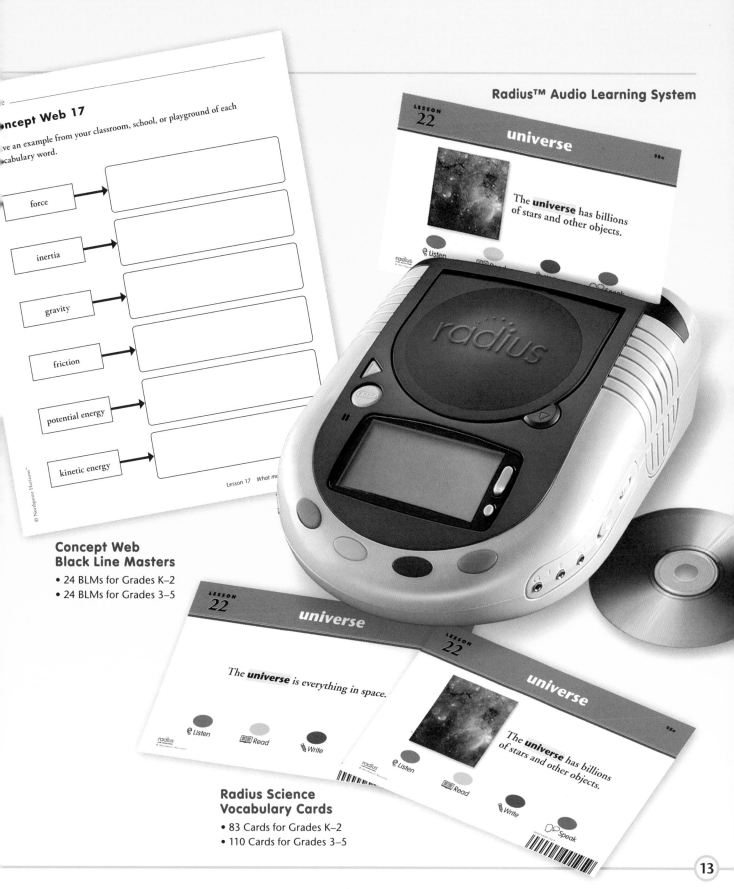

oncept Web 17

ve an example from your classroom, school, or playground of each
cabulary word.

- force →
- inertia →
- gravity →
- friction →
- potential energy →
- kinetic energy →

Lesson 17   What m

© Northpoint Horizons™

Concept Web
Black Line Masters

- 24 BLMs for Grades K–2
- 24 BLMs for Grades 3–5

Radius™ Audio Learning System

LESSON
22
universe

98a

The **universe** has billions
of stars and other objects.

🎧 Listen   📖 Read   ✏️ Write   🗣 Speak

LESSON
22
universe

LESSON
22
universe

The **universe** is everything in space.

🎧 Listen   📖 Read   ✏️ Write

The **universe** has billions
of stars and other objects.

🎧 Listen   📖 Read   ✏️ Write   🗣 Speak

Radius Science
Vocabulary Cards

- 83 Cards for Grades K–2
- 110 Cards for Grades 3–5

STEP 5

Evaluate

Assess and Reinforce Learning

The teacher reviews the vocabulary words with students and assesses learning.

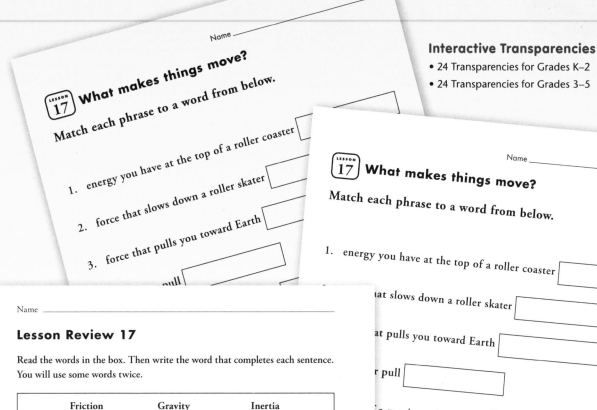

Interactive Transparencies

- 24 Transparencies for Grades K–2
- 24 Transparencies for Grades 3–5

Name _____

17 What makes things move?

Match each phrase to a word from below.

1. energy you have at the top of a roller coaster

2. force that slows down a roller skater

3. force that pulls you toward Earth

Name _____

Lesson Review 17

Read the words in the box. Then write the word that completes each sentence.
You will use some words twice.

Friction	Gravity	Inertia

1. _____ keeps a rock that is not moving from moving.

2. _____ pulls water down a waterfall.

3. _____ makes skates slow down.

4. _____ keeps a golf ball moving.

Write <u>more</u> or <u>less</u> on the line to answer each question.

6. Would a car have more or less potential energy as it moves down a hill?
   It would have _____ potential energy.

7. Would a car have more or less kinetic energy as it moves down a hill?
   It would have _____ kinetic energy.

Give two examples of forces.

8. _____

   _____

Name _____

17 What makes things move?

Match each phrase to a word from below.

1. energy you have at the top of a roller coaster

   at slows down a roller skater

   at pulls you toward Earth

   r pull

   a moving roller coaster

   oving train moving

friction	gravity
kinetic energy	potential energy

Black Line Masters

- 24 BLMs for Grades K–2
- 24 BLMs for Grades 3–5

Lesson Review
Black Line Masters

- 24 BLMs for Grades K–2
- 24 BLMs for Grades 3–5

▲ Northpoint Horizons™   •   866-466-7047   •   www.NorthpointHorizons.com

Grades
K–2 Teacher's Guide

STEP 1

⊙ **Engage**

Focus on Building Background with Concept Poster/ Vocabulary Cards

LESSON 16 | How do things move?

Engage
Concept Poster 6 and Science Vocabulary Cards 55–58 *Whole group activity*

Build Background
Show children side A of card 55 (force) and ask them to find a similar image on the poster. (boy pushing toy train) Place card 55, image side out, in the pocket closest to the image. Say: *The boy is playing with a toy train.* Ask: *What will happen if he pushes or pulls the train?* (It will move.) *What are some different ways the train can move?* (straight, back and forth, in a circle) Read the sentence on side A of the card. Repeat with remaining cards.
Ask children the following questions:
• *What force makes the children on the swings slow down?* (friction)
• *What force makes the girl go down the slide?* (gravity)
• *How do you know the swings are in motion?* (They are moving back and forth.)
• *What is a force?* (a push or pull)

Explore and Learn
Inquiry Activity *Small group activity*

Model the Activity
• Place the materials for Activity Placemat 16 on each table, including copies of Activity Record Sheet 16 (p. 94).
• Model the correct pronunciation for each of the activity materials. Have children repeat the words.
• Read the steps of Activity Placemat 16 (Explore Friction) aloud with children. Model for children the correct way to rub the pieces of paper together.
• Guide children as they work in small groups to complete the activity and Activity Record Sheet 16. Caution children to carefully handle the sandpaper.
• Have each child work with a partner to complete the **Now Try This** activity.

Discuss the Activity
Invite children to discuss the activity and compare observations. Ask:
• *Which kind of paper is the roughest?*
• *Which kind of paper is the smoothest?*
• *What kind of force happened when you rubbed the pieces of paper together?*
• *Which kind of paper warmed your hands the most when you rubbed pieces of it together?*
• *Which kind of paper warmed your hands the least when you rubbed pieces of it together?*

Vocabulary Words
force, friction, gravity, motion

Science Objectives
Children will:
• define force
• describe how the roughness of a surface affects friction
• explain how friction and gravity affect an object's motion
• describe how motion can vary

TESOL/LA Objectives
Children will:
• understand and produce technical vocabulary
• use contextual clues
• follow oral and written directions
• record observations

Materials
• Concept Poster 6
• Science Vocabulary Cards 55–58
• Activity Placemat 16
• Activity Record Sheet 16
• Science Journal
• Science Content Picture Dictionary
• Flip Book Lesson 16
• Concept Web 16
• Radius™ Science Vocabulary Cards 55–58
• Transparency 16
• Lesson Review 16

STEP 2

⊙ **Explore and Learn**

Hands-On Learning with Activity Placemat/ Manipulatives

⊙ Component list for each lesson

STEP
3

⊙ **Explain Concepts and Vocabulary**

Systematic, Direct Instruction through the Flip Book

Explain Concepts and Vocabulary

Flip Book *Whole group activity*

Build Background

Review the Concept Poster 6 activity from the **Engage** section. Ask:
- *How does force affect things on the playground?*
- *How does friction affect things on the playground?*
- *How does gravity affect things on the playground?*
- *Which things in the playground are in motion?*

Read Flip Book, Lesson 16

- Point to the title and read it aloud. Have children repeat the words. Then ask children to brainstorm answers to the title question. If a child uses the word **force,** point to the word on the Flip Book page.
- Read the first sentence, pointing to each word as you read. Have children repeat the words. Point to the middle photo and say: *This photo shows some girls ice skating together.* Read the caption and have children repeat the words. Then ask: *What are the girls doing if they are in motion?* (moving) *What are some ways the girls might move?* (in a circle, back and forth)
- Read the second sentence, pointing to each word as you read. Have children repeat the words. Point to the photo on the left and say: *A force is acting on this ice skater.* Read the caption and have children repeat the words. Then ask: *How does friction affect the skater?* (Friction is pushing against her skates. It can slow down her motion.) Explain to children that friction acts in the direction that is opposite to that of a moving object.
- Point to the photo on the right and say: *A force is acting on this sled.* Read the caption and have children repeat the words. Then ask: *How is gravity acting on the sled?* (Gravity is pulling on it.)

Make Connections

- Point to the **Make Connections** box and read the statement. Then, as a whole group, discuss the motion in each picture. Ask: *How is the race car moving on the race track?* (The car is moving fast in a circle.) *How is the cheetah moving across the ground?* (The cheetah is running fast in a straight line.) *How are the boy and the ball moving?* (The boy is kicking a ball forward.)

Vocabulary Word Wall

Place these words on the Word Wall:

force, friction, gravity, motion

Have children copy the words in their Science Journals. Next, have children draw a picture to illustrate each word. Photocopy and post the children's illustrations below the appropriate words on the Word Wall.

Cognates

For Spanish-speaking children, it may be helpful to post this cognate chart to show similarities between words in Spanish and English. Keep in mind that children have varying literacy levels in Spanish, and some may not be familiar with these words.

Cognates	
English	Spanish
force	fuerza
friction	fricción
gravity	gravedad
motion	movimiento
paper	papel

Science Content Picture Dictionary

For children needing additional help with vocabulary words, refer them to the Science Content Picture Dictionary.

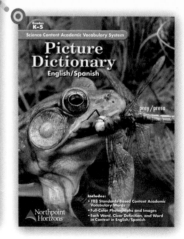

Grades K–5
Science Content Academic Vocabulary System
Picture Dictionary
English/Spanish

prey/presa

Includes:
- TBB Standard-Based Content Academic Vocabulary Words
- Full-Color Photographs and Images
- Each Word, Clear Definition, and Word in Context in English/Spanish

Northpoint Horizons

Elaborate

Concept Web *Paired activity*

Distribute copies of Concept Web 16 (p. 95). Have each child work with a partner to complete the concept web. For children needing additional help with the web, refer them to the Concept Poster 6, Science Vocabulary Cards 55–58, and the Flip Book. When children have finished, ask volunteers to share and talk about their completed webs.

Radius™ Science Vocabulary Cards
Small group activity

Have children use the Radius™ Audio Learning System and Radius™ Science Vocabulary Cards 55–58 to practice listening to, reading, writing, and speaking each word. Then have children do one or more of the following activities in their Science Journals:

- Have children look in magazines and newspapers for pictures that illustrate the vocabulary words: force, friction, gravity, motion. Tell them to cut out the pictures and paste them into their Science Journals. Then have them use the vocabulary words as labels in their pictures. For example, children might find a picture of a basketball falling through a hoop to go with *motion* and *gravity*.
- Encourage children to think about sports they have played or watched. Tell them that force is involved in sports. Ask them to write sentences describing how force is used in some popular sports. Write completion sentences such as these on the board for children to write and complete: The batter uses force to _____ a _____. The kicker uses force to _____ a _____.
- Ask children to look for things in the classroom or outside that are in motion. Have them work with a partner to write a list of things in motion.

Evaluate

Transparency 16 *Whole group activity*

Assess Vocabulary Knowledge

Use side B (definition side) of the Science Vocabulary Cards 55–58 to review the lesson vocabulary words. Then distribute a copy of Transparency 16 to each child. Have children cut out the vocabulary words at the bottom of the page and place them in the correct boxes. Model the task for them by using Transparency 16. Invite volunteers to use each vocabulary word in a sentence.

Lesson Review 16 *Individual activity*

Assess Concept Knowledge

Distribute copies of Lesson Review 16 (p. 96). Read the directions aloud and verify children's understanding. For children whose literacy skills are emerging, consider reading the sentences aloud. When finished, review the correct answers with children.

Home Connection

Send the completed copy of Activity Record Sheet 16 (p. 94) home with each child to share with his or her family.

Send a second copy of Transparency 16 home with each child for extra review and practice. Encourage children to work with family members to cut out and place vocabulary words in the appropriate places on the transparency copy. Children can use the transparency copy to review vocabulary words throughout the school year.

 Take-Home Activities

STEP 4

 Elaborate

Practice reading, writing, listening, and speaking each vocabulary word with the Radius Audio Learning System

STEP 5

 Evaluate

Review, reinforce, and assess vocabulary and concept knowledge

Grades K–2
Content Academic Vocabulary for Science

Life Science	Earth Science	Physical Science	Space Science
adaptation	cloud	attract	axis
amphibian	condensation	energy	day
bird	dinosaur	force	experiment
camouflage	erosion	friction	Moon
consumer	evaporation	gas	Moon phases
egg	fossil	gravity	night
environment	investigate	heat	orbit
fish	natural resource	light	planet
flower	pollution	liquid	rotation
food	precipitation	loudness	scientific methods
food chain	season	magnetic force	shadow
food web	temperature	mass	solar system
habitat	thermometer	matter	star
larva	water cycle	mixture	Sun
leaf	weather	motion	
life cycle	weathering	pitch	
living thing		pole	
mammal		reflect	
nonliving thing		repel	
predator		solid	
prey		vibrate	
producer			
pupa			
reptile			
root			
seed			
shelter			
stem			
tadpole			

LESSON
16
force

A **force** can make objects move.

Northpoint Horizons

LESSON
16
motion

Ice skaters moving across the ice are in **motion.**

LESSON
16
gravity

Gravity pulls a sled downhill.

57a

Northpoint Horizons

Northpoint Horizons™   •   866-466-7047   •   www.NorthpointHorizons.com

Grades
3–5 Teacher's Guide

STEP 1

⊙ **Engage**
Focus on Building Background with Concept Poster/ Vocabulary Cards

LESSON 17 What makes things move?

Engage
Concept Poster 6 and Science Vocabulary Cards 74–79 *Whole group activity*

Build Background
Show students side A of card 74 (force) and ask them to find a similar image on the poster. (water pushing down slide, boy's arms pushing merry-go-round, children's legs pushing paddle boats, man's arms pulling up flag, children's legs pushing see-saw up and down) Place card 74, image side out, in the pocket closest to the image. Say: *A force is a push or pull. How is the boy's foot acting as a force in the picture on this card?* (pushing/kicking ball) *Do you see any other examples of pushing or pulling on the poster?* (see examples above) Read the sentence on side A of the card. Repeat with remaining cards.
Ask students the following questions:
* *Earth's force of gravity pulls down on all matter. What would happen if Earth had no gravity?* (everything would float upward)
* *The force of inertia keeps an object moving or keeps an object motionless until a force acts on it. What objects in the picture are not moving?* (buildings, equipment, and any people who are standing still)
* *Friction is a force between objects rubbing together that slows down their motion. Give an example of friction.*
* *What kind of energy does a moving object have?* (kinetic energy) *An object that is not moving?* (potential energy)

Explore and Learn
Inquiry Activity *Small group activity*

Model the Activity
* Place the materials for Activity Placemat 17 on each table, including copies of Activity Record Sheet 17 (p. 100).
* Model the correct pronunciation for each of the activity materials. Have students repeat the words. Explain that they are going to observe the force of friction when an inflated balloon deflates inside a shoebox.
* Read the steps of Activity Placemat 17 (Observe Friction) aloud with students.
* Guide students as they work in small groups to complete the activity and Activity Record Sheet 17.
* Have student partners complete the **Now Try This** activity.

Discuss the Activity
Invite students to discuss the activity and compare observations. Ask:
* *What happened when you let the balloon go?*
* *How much did your shoebox move?*
* *What happened when you used sandpaper and repeated the test?*

Vocabulary Words
force, inertia, gravity, friction, potential energy, kinetic energy

Science Objectives
Students will:
* recognize that force is a push or pull on an object
* compare the forces of gravity and friction
* describe the relationship between force and inertia
* discuss the difference between potential energy and kinetic energy
* observe the force of friction acting on a moving shoebox
* measure the movement of the shoebox on wax paper and sandpaper

TESOL/LA Objectives
Students will:
* explore alternative ways of saying things
* test hypotheses about language
* negotiate and manage interaction to manage tasks
* ask for assistance with a task

Materials
* Concept Poster 6
* Science Vocabulary Cards 74–79
* Activity Placemat 17
* Activity Record Sheet 17
* Science Journal
* Science Content Picture Dictionary
* Reader Cards 17A, 17B
* Concept Web 17
* Radius™ Science Vocabulary Cards 74–79
* Transparency 17
* Lesson Review 17

STEP 2

⊙ **Explore and Learn**
Hands-On Learning with Activity Placemat/ Manipulatives

⊙ Component list for each lesson

Lesson 17   *What makes things move?*   **97**

STEP
3

Explain Concepts and Vocabulary

Reader Cards A and B *Whole group, small group, and paired activities*

Build Background

Review the Concept Poster 6 activity from the **Engage** section. Ask:
- *What forces are acting on the boy on the water slide?* (gravity and friction)
- *What is the force of gravity?* (force that pulls all matter toward Earth)
- *Suppose the merry-go-round in the picture were spinning in outer space. Why would it keep spinning?* (inertia would keep it spinning because there would be no gravity or friction to slow it down)
- *Explain how the force of friction works between the boy's body and the water slide.* (contact between the boy's body and the slide cause friction which slows down his motion)
- *Explain this statement: All objects have energy.* (All objects have stored energy—potential—and the energy of motion—kinetic.)

Read the Reader Cards A and B

- Distribute copies of the Reader Cards to students. Give Reader Card A to Beginning/Emerging English learners and Card B to Intermediate/Expanding English learners and native English speakers.
- Direct students' attention to the title of the card and read it aloud. Have students repeat the words. Then ask students to brainstorm answers to the title question. Encourage students to use lesson vocabulary words in their answers.
- Have students preview the pictures on the Reader Card and describe what they see. Ask them: *What kind of movement do you see in the pictures? What forces are causing the movement?* Then have students read the Reader Card aloud in a small group or with a partner. Vary the groups and partners whenever possible to provide broad conversation practice for English learners. Note that new English speakers may be able to read only single words.
- Encourage students to check one another's comprehension by responding to the questions or prompts located next to the Talk icons.
- Circulate among students, guiding them and providing assistance as needed.

Make Connections

- Direct students' attention to the **Make Connections** boxes. Tell students to work with their partners to discuss the questions or prompts, or to complete the activities.
- Suggest that students use their Science Journal to record responses or observations.

Vocabulary Word Wall

Place these words on the Word Wall:

force, inertia, gravity, friction, potential energy, kinetic energy

Have students copy the words in their Science Journals. Then have students draw a picture to illustrate each word and write a sentence using the word. Photocopy and post examples of students' illustrations and sentences below the appropriate words on the Word Wall.

Cognates

For Spanish-speaking students, it may be helpful to post this cognate chart to show similarities between vocabulary words in Spanish and English. Keep in mind that students have varying literacy levels in Spanish, and some may not be familiar with these words.

Cognates	
English	**Spanish**
force	fuerza
inertia	inercia
gravity	gravedad
friction	fricción
potential energy	energía potencial
kinetic energy	energía cinética

Science Content Picture Dictionary

For students needing additional help with vocabulary words, refer them to the Science Content Picture Dictionary.

Explain Concepts and Vocabulary

Systematic, Direct Instruction through reading and discussing the information in the Reader Cards

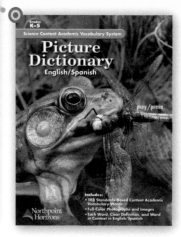

Grades K–5
Science Content Academic Vocabulary System

Picture Dictionary
English/Spanish

prey/presa

Includes:
- 188 Standards-Based Content Academic Vocabulary Words
- Full-Color Photographs and Images
- Each Word, Clear Definition, and Word in Context in English/Spanish

Northpoint Horizons

Elaborate

Concept Web *Paired activity*

Distribute copies of Concept Web 17 (p. 101). Have each student work with a partner to discuss the words and complete the web. For students needing additional help with the web, refer them to the Concept Poster 6, Science Vocabulary Cards 74–79, and Reader Cards A and B. When students have finished, ask volunteers to share and talk about their completed webs.

Radius™ Science Vocabulary Cards
Small group activity

Have students use the Radius™ Audio Learning System and Radius™ Science Vocabulary Cards 74–79 to practice listening to, reading, writing, and speaking each vocabulary word. Then have students do one or more of the following activities in their Science Journals:

- Ask students to write sentences about gravity, potential energy, friction, and kinetic energy. Write a model sentence for them to follow on the board: When you push a heavy desk across the floor, there is _____ when the legs of the desk rub against the floor. (friction)
- Invite students to use their own words to write definitions of the vocabulary words. Have them illustrate their definitions.

Evaluate

Transparency 17 *Whole group activity*

Assess Vocabulary Knowledge
Use side B (definition side) of the Science Vocabulary Cards 74–79 to review the lesson vocabulary words. Then distribute a copy of Transparency 17 to each student. Have students cut out the words at the bottom of the page and place them in the correct boxes. Model the task for them by using Transparency 17. Invite volunteers to use each vocabulary word in a sentence.

Lesson Review 17 *Individual activity*

Assess Concept Knowledge
Distribute copies of Lesson Review 17 (p. 102). Read the directions aloud and verify students' understanding. For students whose literacy skills in English are emerging, consider reading the sentences aloud. When students have finished, review the correct answers.

Home Connection
Send the completed copy of Activity Record Sheet 17 (p. 100) home with each student to share with his or her family.

Send a second copy of Transparency 17 home with each student for extra review and practice. Encourage students to work with family members to cut out and place vocabulary words in the appropriate places on the transparency copy. Students can use the transparency copy to review vocabulary words throughout the school year.

 Take-Home Activities

STEP 4

 Elaborate

Practice reading, writing, listening, and speaking each vocabulary word with the Radius Audio Learning System

STEP 5

 Evaluate

Review, reinforce, and assess vocabulary and concept knowledge

Lesson 17 *What makes things move?* **99**

Grades 3–5
Content Academic Vocabulary for Science

Life Science	Earth Science	Physical Science	Space Science
adaptation	atmosphere	absorb	axis
carnivore	condensation	atoms	constellation
cell	conservation	change of state	equator
class	core	chemical change	galaxy
community	crust	compound	lunar eclipse
decomposer	deposition	conduction	Moon phase
ecosystem	earthquake	convection	planet
embryo	epicenter	density	revolution
energy pyramid	erosion	electric change	rotation
extinction	evaporation	electric circuit	scientific methods
herbivore	fault	electric current	solar eclipse
inherited	igneous rock	element	solar system
kingdom	investigation	energy transfer	universe
microscope	landform	experiment	
nucleus	landslide	force	
omnivore	lava	friction	
organ	magma	fulcrum	
organ system	mantle	gravity	
organism	metamorphic rock	inclined plane	
ovary	natural resource	inertia	
photosynthesis	nonrenewable	kinetic energy	
phylum	resource	lever	
pistil	plate	mass	
pollen	pollution	mixture	
pollination	precipitation	physical change	
population	recycle	potential energy	
protist	renewable resource	pulley	
species	sedimentary rock	radiation	
spore	topography	reflect	
stamen	volcano	refract	
tissue	water cycle	safety	
	weathering	solution	
		thermal	
		volume	
		wheel and axle	

LESSON 17 friction

Friction causes the boy's skates to slow down.

Northpoint Horizons

LESSON 17 gravity

Gravity pulls the water in a waterfall down.

76

LESSON 17 kinetic energy

Potential energy changes to **kinetic energy** as the roller coaster moves down the track.

Northpoint Horizons

79a

(23)

Science CAVS ™

Content Academic Vocabulary System (CAVS) is the perfect solution for all students who have difficulty with the vocabulary critical for understanding Science concepts and comprehending Science texts.

CAVS is ideal for English Language Learners, Title I Pull-Out Programs, Resource Classrooms, Response-to-Intervention, and Special Education.

CAVS is available in 4 packages.

K–2 CAVS for Science
N978-1-60410-700-5

3–5 CAVS for Science
N978-1-60410-724-1

K–2 CAVS for Math
N978-1-60410-850-7

3–5 CAVS for Math
N978-1-60410-874-3

For prices and ordering information:

Call Northpoint Horizons **866.466.7047**
Or email **CustomerService@NorthpointHorizons.com**

www.NorthpointHorizons.com

Northpoint Horizons™

Dedicated to the success of the struggling student.

Science CAVS — Content Academic Vocabulary System

Science K–2
Teacher's Guide

▲ Northpoint Horizons

1-866-466-7047
www.NorthpointHorizons.com
978-1-60410-719-7

Credits

Science K–2 Teacher's Guide

Northpoint Horizons™ would like to thank Kaye Wiley Maggart for her involvement in the development of the Content Academic Vocabulary System:

Kaye Wiley Maggart
ESL Author/Consultant
Hamden, Connecticut

FLIP BOOK

COVER: butterfly ©Darrell Gulin/Corbis; turtle ©Larry L. Miller/Photo Researchers, Inc.; erosion ©Corey Hochachka/AGE Fotostock; gravity ©Stone/Getty Images; solar system illustration: Stephen Durke **LESSON 1:** seed ©Pixtal/AGE Fotostock; panda ©Daniel J. Cox/Corbis; toy duck ©Dorling Kindersley/Getty Images; rock ©Dean Uhlinger/Corbis **Make Connections** pebbles ©Gusto/Photo Researchers, Inc.; lion ©George Calef/Masterfile; butterfly ©Darrell Gulin/Corbis; lava lamp ©Pierre Tremblay/Masterfile; dog ©Gail Shumway/Getty Images **LESSON 2:** plants ©Phil Degginger/Alamy; seeds ©Black Box, Inc.; new plant ©Holt Studios International Ltd/Alamy **Make Connections** plant A ©blickwinkel/Alamy; plant B ©blickwinkel/Alamy; plant C ©blickwinkel/Alamy; plant D ©blickwinkel/Alamy **LESSON 3:** amphibian ©Kenneth H. Thomas/Photo Researchers, Inc.; skeleton ©PhotoLink/AGE Fotostock; bird ©Gerard Lacz/Animals Animals; reptile ©Creatas/AGE Fotostock; fish ©Georgie Holland/AGE Fotostock; mammal ©Mark J. Barrett/Alamy **Make Connections** dog ©Thorsten Milse/Robert Harding World Imagery/Corbis; fish ©Papilio/Alamy; chameleon ©Photodisc/AGE Fotostock; eagle ©Johan Swanepoel/Alamy; frog ©Rod Planck/Photo Researchers, Inc. **LESSON 4:** frog ©Bouve Francois/AGE Fotostock; eggs ©Nuridsany & Perennou/Photo Researchers, Inc.; tadpole in egg ©Nuridsany & Perennou/Photo Researchers, Inc.; tadpole ©Nuridsany & Perennou/Photo Researchers, Inc.; tadpole with legs ©Nuridsany & Perennou/Photo Researchers, Inc. **Make Connections** eggs ©E. R. Degginger/Animals Animals; tadpole ©Breck P. Kent/Animals Animals; tadpole with legs ©Breck P. Kent/Animals Animals; frog ©Michael Gadomski/Animals Animals **LESSON 5:** butterfly ©Don Farrall/AGE Fotostock; egg ©George D. Lepp/Photo Researchers, Inc.; larva ©Scott Camazine/Photo Researchers, Inc.; pupa (right) ©Scott Camazine/Photo Researchers, Inc.; pupa (left) ©Scott Camazine/Photo Researchers, Inc.; butterfly emerging ©Scott Camazine/Photo Researchers, Inc. **Make Connections** pupa ©David M. Dennis/Animals Animals; butterfly ©David M. Dennis/Animals Animals; egg ©David M. Dennis/Animals Animals; larva ©David M. Dennis/Animals Animals **LESSON 6:** rabbit ©Antinolo Jorge Sierra/Animals Animals; bunnies in nest ©OSF/Animals Animals; bunny ©William Paton/OSF/Animals Animals **Make Connections** bunnies ©Adam Jones/Photo Researchers, Inc.; rabbit ©Leonard Lee Rue III/Photo Researchers, Inc.; bunnies in nest ©Scott Camazine/Photo Researchers, Inc. **LESSON 7:** forest scene illustration: Dan Burr; mushrooms ©Chris Mattison/SuperStock; birds ©Terrance Klassen/SuperStock; bat ©David A. Northcott/Corbis; raccoon ©Corbis; insect ©Corbis **Make Connections** shelter ©Bob Bowdey/SuperStock; camouflage ©SuperStock; adaptation ©G. Ronald Austing/Photo Researchers, Inc. **LESSON 8:** swamp scene illustration: Dan Burr; frog ©Visuals Unlimited/Corbis; alligator ©Creatas/AGE Fotostock; turtle ©Larry L. Miller/Photo Researchers, Inc.; water lily ©Klaus Nigge/Getty Images; snake ©Brian P. Kenney/Animals Animals **Make Connections** bird ©Arthur Morris/Corbis; turtle ©John Cancalosi/AGE Fotostock **LESSON 9:** water cycle illustration: Wendy Smith; **Make Connections** puddle ©Pixtal/SuperStoc; clouds ©Photos.com; water ©Photos.com **LESSON 10:** hot ©Photonica/Getty Images; cold ©Carson Ganci/AGE Fotostock; wet ©altrendo images/Getty Images; windy ©Brian Sytnyk/Masterfile **Make Connections** rain ©Thomas Wiewandt/Getty Images; sun ©Hiroshi Takano/AGE Fotostock **LESSON 11:** weathering ©Photonica/Getty Images; pollution ©Jean-Marc Charles/AGE Fotostock; erosion ©Corey Hochachka/AGE Fotostock **Make Connections** erosion ©Ioseba Egibar/AGE Fotostock; pollution ©Steve Allen/Jupiter Images; weathering ©Photos.com **LESSON 12:** thermometer illustrations: Jason Wasmiller; spring ©Gary Buss/Getty Images; summer ©Gary Buss/Getty Images; autumn ©Gary Buss/Getty Images; winter ©Gary Buss/Getty Images **Make Connections** spring ©Ariel Skelley/AGE Fotostock; autumn ©Ariel Skelley/AGE Fotostock; summer ©Dave & Les Jacobs/AGE Fotostock **LESSON 13:** scientists ©Louie Psihoyos/Corbis; skeleton ©Paul A. Souders/Corbis; egg ©Louie Psihoyos/Corbis; teeth ©Louie Psihoyos/Corbis; footprint ©Tom Till/Alamy **Make Connections** fern ©Breck P. Kent/Animals Animals - Earth Scenes; fish ©Breck P. Kent/Animals Animals - Earth Scenes; shell ©Laurance Richardson/Alamy; starfish ©Breck P. Kent/Animals Animals - Earth Scenes; dragonfly ©AGE Fotostock/SuperStock **LESSON 14:** kids ©Tim Fuller **Make Connections** truck ©Getty Images; apple ©Photos.com; shoes ©Photos.com **LESSON 15:** fish tank illustration: Kristen Kest; **Make Connections** fishbowl ©Photographer's Choice/Getty Images; air ©Photographer's Choice/Getty Images; stones ©Colin Paterson/SuperStock **LESSON 16:** winter scene illustration: Laura Jacobsen; friction ©Rick Gomez/Masterfile; motion ©Iconica/Getty Images; gravity ©Stone/Getty Images **Make Connections** racecar ©kolvenbach/Alamy; ©Steve Bloom Images/Alamy; boy ©Stone/Getty Images **LESSON 17:** magnet illustrations: Precision Graphics; train ©Photos.com **LESSON 18:** camping scene illustration: Stacey Schuett; **Make Connections** firefly ©Phil Degginger/Alamy; flashlight ©Comstock/SuperStock; sun ©Photos.com; rocks ©The Image Bank/Getty Images **LESSON 19:** fire ©Getty Images; oven ©Getty Images; ice ©Jim Wileman/Alamy **Make Connections** oven ©Liane Cary/AGE Fotostock; lamp ©Photos.com; toaster ©C. V. D'Andrea/AGE Fotostock **LESSON 20:** guitar ©Photos.com; coyote ©David W. Middleton/SuperStock; girl ©Jose Luis Pelaez, Inc/Jupiter Images **Make Connections** lawn mower ©Comstock/Jupiter Images; leaves ©Getty Images; whistle ©Stone/Getty Images; drum ©Getty Images **LESSON 21:** kids ©Tim Fuller **Make Connections** boy ©image100/Corbis; umbrella ©Getty Images; girl ©Stock Connection Distribution/Alamy; pear © Ian Goodrick/Alamy **LESSON 22:** nighttime scene illustration: Mary Teichman; moon phases ©Guy Grenier/Masterfile **Make Connections** night sky ©Mauritius/SuperStock; half moon ©Eckhard Slawik/Photo Researchers, Inc.; full moon ©Eckhard Slawik/Photo Researchers, Inc. **LESSON 23:** Earth's rotation illustrations: Stephen Durke **LESSON 24:** solar system illustration: Stephen Durke; scientist ©1989 Roger Ressmeyer: with Ian Shelton/Corbis **Make Connections** Saturn ©Science Faction/Getty Images; soccer ball ©Photos.com; moon ©J & C Sohns/AGE Fotostock; Earth ©NASA

SCIENCE VOCABULARY CARDS AND RADIUS™ SCIENCE VOCABULARY CARDS, K–2

LESSON 1: living thing ©Daniel J. Cox/Corbis; nonliving thing ©Dean Uhlinger/Corbis **LESSON 2:** life cycle (clockwise from left) ©Phil Degginger/Alamy; ©Black Box, Inc.; ©Holt Studios International Ltd/Alamy; seed ©Black Box, Inc.; root ©Phil Degginger/Alamy; stem ©Phil Degginger/Alamy; leaf ©Phil Degginger/Alamy; flower ©Phil Degginger/Alamy **LESSON 3:** amphibian ©Kenneth H. Thomas/Photo Researchers, Inc.; bird ©Gerard Lacz/Animals Animals; reptile ©Creatas/AGE Fotostock; fish ©Georgie Holland/AGE Fotostock; mammal ©Mark J. Barrett/Alamy **LESSON 4:** life cycle (clockwise from left) ©Bouve Francois/AGE Fotostock; ©Nuridsany & Perennou/Photo Researchers, Inc.; ©Nuridsany & Perennou/Photo Researchers, Inc.; ©Nuridsany & Perennou/Photo Researchers, Inc.; ©Nuridsany & Perennou/Photo Researchers, Inc.; egg ©Nuridsany & Perennou/Photo Researchers, Inc.; tadpole ©Nuridsany & Perennou/Photo Researchers, Inc. **LESSON 5:** life cycle (clockwise from left) ©Don Farrall/AGE Fotostock; ©George D. Lepp/Photo Researchers, Inc.; Scott Camazine/Photo Researchers, Inc.; ©Scott Camazine/Photo Researchers, Inc.; ©Scott Camazine/Photo Researchers, Inc.; larva ©Scott Camazine/Photo Researchers, Inc.; pupa (left) ©Scott Camazine/Photo Researchers, Inc.; (right) ©Scott Camazine/Photo Researchers, Inc. **LESSON 6:** life cycle (clockwise from left) ©Antinolo Jorge Sierra/Animals Animals; ©OSF/Animals Animals; ©William Paton/OSF/Animals Animals **LESSON 7:** environment forest scene illustration by Dan Burr; habitat ©Chris Mattison/SuperStock; adaption ©Terrance Klassen/SuperStock; camouflage ©Corbis; shelter ©Corbis **LESSON 8:** food ©John Cancalosi/AGE Fotostock; food chain (from left) ©Klaus Nigge/Getty Images; ©Larry L. Miller/Photo Researchers, Inc.; ©Creatas/AGE Fotostock; food web (clockwise from left) ©Visuals Unlimited/Corbis; ©Creatas/AGE Fotostock; ©Larry L. Miller/Photo Researchers, Inc.; ©Klaus Nigge/Getty Images; ©Brian P. Kenney/Animals Animals; prey ©Visuals Unlimited/Corbis; predator ©Creatas/AGE Fotostock; producer ©Klaus Nigge/Getty Images; consumer ©Larry L. Miller/Photo Researchers, Inc. **LESSON 9:** illustrations by Wendy Smith **LESSON 10:** weather ©altrendo images/Getty Images **LESSON 11:** weathering ©Photonica/Getty Images; erosion ©Corey Hochachka/AGE Fotostock; pollution ©Steve Allen/Jupiter Images **LESSON 12:** season ©Gary Buss/Getty Images; temperature ©Dave & Les Jacobs/AGE Fotostock; thermometer illustration by Jason Wasmiller **LESSON 13:** investigate ©Louie Psihoyos/Corbis; dinosaur ©Paul A. Souders/Corbis; fossil ©Tom Till/Alamy **LESSON 14:** matter ©Tim Fuller; mass ©Black Box, Inc. **LESSON 15:** illustrations by Kristin Kest **LESSON 16:** force ©Stone/Getty Images; friction ©Rick Gomez/Masterfile; gravity ©Stone/Getty Images; motion ©Iconica/Getty Images **LESSON 17:** magnetic force ©Photos.com; illustrations Precision Graphics **LESSON 18:** illustrations Stacey Schuett **LESSON 19:** heat ©Getty Images **LESSON 20:** vibrate ©Photos.com; loudness ©David W. Middleton/SuperStock; pitch ©Jose Luis Pelaez, Inc/Jupiter Images **LESSON 21:** Sun ©Photos.com; day ©Tim Fuller; experiment ©Tim Fuller; shadow ©Tim Fuller **LESSON 22:** night ©Mauritius/SuperStock; Moon ©Eckhard Slawik/Photo Researchers, Inc.; Moon phase ©Guy Grenier/Masterfile; star ©Mauritius/SuperStock **LESSON 23:** illustrations Stephen Durke **LESSON 24:** planet ©NASA; solar system illustration by Stephen Durke; scientific methods ©1989 Roger Ressmeyer; with Ian Shelton/Corbis

CONCEPT POSTERS, K–2

Poster 1 (Lessons 1–3): illustration by Kristin Kest **Poster 2 (Lessons 4–6):** illustration by Virge Kask **Poster 3 (Lessons 7–8):** illustration by Christina Wald **Poster 4 (Lessons 9–13):** illustration by Tom Newsom **Poster 5 (Lessons 14–15):** illustration by Tom Newsom **Poster 6 (Lessons 16–17):** illustration by Joel Spector **Poster 7 (Lessons 18–20):** illustration by Higgins Bond **Poster 8 (Lessons 21–24):** illustration by Greg Copeland

TRANSPARENCIES, K–2 illustrations by Christen Stewart; page 23 Rolin Graphics

SCIENCE CONTENT PICTURE DICTIONARY

Page 1: absorb illustration by Precision Graphics adaptation ©Terrance Klassen/SuperStock amphibian ©Kenneth H. Thomas/Photo Researchers, Inc. **Page 2:** atmosphere ©Digital Vision/Getty Images atom illustration by Precision Graphics attract illustration by Precision Graphics **Page 3:** axis illustration by Stephen Durke bird ©Gerard Lacz/Animals Animals camouflage ©Corbis **Page 4:** carnivore ©Photos.com cell illustration by Frank Ippolito change of state ©Ernest Manewal/SuperStock **Page 5:** chemical change ©Javier Larrea/AGE Fotostock class illustration by Sharon & Joel Harris cloud illustration by Wendy Smith **Page 6:** community ©Digital Vision/Getty Images compound - left ©PHOTOTAKE Inc./Alamy; center ©Yoav Levy/Phototake; right ©Tom Grill/Corbis condensation illustration by Wendy Smith **Page 7:** conduction ©Rod Planck/Photo Researchers, Inc. conservation ©Robb Gregg constellation ©Robert Karpa/Masterfile **Page 8:** consumer ©Larry L. Miller/Photo Researchers, Inc. convection ©Food Features/Alamy core illustration by Chuck Carter **Page 9:** crust illustration by Chuck Carter day ©Tim Fuller decomposer ©Photos.com **Page 10:** density ©Black Box, Inc. deposition illustration by Precision Graphics dinosaur ©Paul A. Souders/Corbis **Page 11:** earthquake ©Lloyd Cluff/Corbis ecosystem ©Gabriela Staebler/zefa/Corbis egg ©Nuridsany & Perennou/Photo Researchers, Inc. **Page 12:** electric charge ©Roy McMahon/Corbis electric circuit ©Black Box, Inc. electric current ©Jack Novak/SuperStock **Page 13:** element ©Lester Lefkowitz/Getty Images embryo ©Black Box, Inc. energy illustration by Stacey Schuett **Page 14:** energy pyramid illustration by Frank Ippolito energy transfer ©Carson Ganci/AGE Fotostock environment illustration by Dan Burr **Page 15:** epicenter illustration by Chuck Carter equator illustration by Stephen Durke erosion ©Corey Hochachka/AGE Fotostock **Page 16:** evaporation illustration by Wendy Smith experiment ©Tim Fuller extinction illustration by Nathan Hale **Page 17:** fault ©The Stocktrek Corp/Jupiter Images fish ©Georgie Holland/AGE Fotostock flower ©Phil Degginger/Alamy **Page 18:** food ©John Cancalosi/AGE Fotostock food chain - top ©Klaus Nigge/Getty Images; center ©Larry L. Miller/ Photo Researchers, Inc.; bottom ©Creatas/AGE Fotostock food web - clockwise from top left ©Visuals Unlimited/Corbis; ©Creatas/AGE Fotostock; ©Larry L. Miller/Photo Researchers, Inc.; ©Klaus Nigge/Getty Images; ©Brian P. Kenney/Animals Animals **Page 19:** force ©Stone/Getty Images fossil ©Tom Till/Alamy friction ©Rick Gomez/Masterfile **Page 20:** fulcrum ©Ariel Skelley/Corbis galaxy ©NASA gas illustration by Kristin Kest **Page 21:** gravity ©Stone/Getty Images habitat ©Chris Mattison/SuperStock heat ©Getty Images **Page 22:** herbivore ©Photos.com igneous rock ©Purestock/Getty Images inclined plane ©Tim Pannell/Corbis **Page 23:** inertia ©Digital Vision/Getty Images inherited ©Pankaj & Insy Shah/AGE Fotostock investigate ©Louie Psihoyos/Corbis **Page 24:** investigation ©G. Brad Lewis/Getty Images kinetic energy ©William Manning/Corbis kingdom illustration by Sharon & Joel Harris **Page 25:** landform ©Enrique R. Aguirre/AGE Fotostock landslide ©Reuters/Corbis larva ©Scott Camazine/Photo Researchers, Inc. **Page 26:** lava ©Jim Sugar/Corbis leaf ©Phil Degginger/Alamy lever ©Hugh Threlfall/Alamy **Page 27:** life cycle - frog ©Bouve Francois/AGE Fotostock; all other images ©Nuridsany & Perennou/Photo Researchers, Inc. light illustration by Stacey Schuett liquid illustration by Kristin Kest **Page 28:** living thing ©Daniel J. Cox/Corbis loudness ©David W. Middleton/SuperStock lunar eclipse illustration by Stephen Durke **Page 29:** magnetic force ©Photos.com magma illustration by Stephen Durke mammal ©Mark J. Barrett/Alamy **Page 30:** mantle illustration by Chuck Carter mass ©Black Box, Inc. matter ©Tim Fuller **Page 31:** metamorphic rock ©David Muench/Corbis microscope ©Mark Harmel/Getty Images mixture illustration by Kristin Kest **Page 32:** Moon ©Eckhard Slawik/Photo Researchers, Inc. Moon phase ©Guy Grenier/Masterfile motion ©Iconica/Getty Images **Page 33:** natural resource illustration by Wendy Smith night ©Mauritius/SuperStock nonliving thing ©Dean Uhlinger/Corbis **Page 34:** nonrenewable resource ©AGE Fotostock/SuperStock nucleus ©Eric V. Grave/Photo Researchers, Inc. omnivore - top ©Joe McDonald/Corbis; bottom ©Corbis/AGE Fotostock **Page 35:** orbit illustration by Stephen Durke organ illustration by Sharon & Joel Harris organ system illustration by Sharon & Joel Harris **Page 36:** organism ©Photos.com ovary ©E. R. Degginger/Photo Researchers, Inc. photosynthesis illustration by Virge Kask **Page 37:** phylum illustration by Sharon & Joel Harris physical change ©Digital Vision/Getty Images pistil ©E. R. Degginger/Photo Researchers, Inc. **Page 38:** pitch ©Jose Luis Pelaez, Inc/Jupiter Images planet ©NASA plate illustration by Precision Graphics **Page 39:** pole illustration by Precision Graphics pollen ©E. R. Degginger/Photo Researchers, Inc. pollination illustration by Kristin Kest **Page 40:** pollution ©Jean-Marc Charles/AGE Fotostock population ©jonathan & angela/Getty Images potential energy ©Kelly-Mooney Photography/Corbis **Page 41:** precipitation illustration by Wendy Smith predator ©Creatas/AGE Fotostock prey ©Visuals Unlimited/Corbis **Page 42:** producer ©Klaus Nigge/Getty Images protist ©Eric V. Grave/Photo Researchers, Inc. pulley - top ©Gary John Norman/Getty Images; bottom ©Neil Rabinowitz/ Corbis **Page 43:** pupa ©Scott Camazine/Photo Researchers, Inc. radiation ©Rod Planck/Photo Researchers, Inc. recycle ©Richard Hutchings/Corbis **Page 44:** reflect illustration by Precision Graphics refract illustration by Precision Graphics renewable resource - top ©Photos.com; center ©Photos.com; bottom ©Don Klumpp/Getty Images **Page 45:** repel illustration by Precision Graphics reptile ©Creatas/AGE Fotostock revolution illustration by Stephen Durke **Page 46:** root ©Phil Degginger/Alamy rotation illustration by Stephen Durke safety ©Robb Gregg **Page 47:** scientific methods ©1989 Roger Ressmeyer; with Ian Shelton/Corbis season ©Gary Buss/Getty Images sedimentary rock ©Photos.com **Page 48:** seed ©Black Box, Inc. shadow ©Tim Fuller shelter ©Corbis **Page 49:** solar eclipse illustration by Stephen Durke solar system illustration by Stephen Durke solid illustration by Kristin Kest **Page 50:** solution ©Clive Streeter/Dorling Kindersley/Getty Images species illustration by Sharon & Joel Harris spore ©Eye of Science/Photo Researchers, Inc. **Page 51:** stamen ©E. R. Degginger/Photo Researchers, Inc. star ©Mauritius/SuperStock stem ©Phil Degginger/Alamy **Page 52:** sun ©Photos.com tadpole ©Nuridsany & Perennou/Photo Researchers, Inc. temperature ©Dave & Les Jacobs/AGE Fotostock **Page 53:** thermal ©Carson Ganci/AGE Fotostock thermometer illustration by Jason Wasmiller tissue ©Visuals Unlimited/Corbis **Page 54:** topography ©Photos.com universe ©NASA vibrate ©Photos.com **Page 55:** volcano illustration by Precision Graphics volume ©Black Box, Inc. water cycle illustration by Wendy Smith **Page 56:** weather ©altrendo images/Getty Images weathering ©Frank Krahmer/Getty Images wheel and axle ©Steve Vidler/SuperStock

TEACHER'S GUIDE

Cover: butterfly ©Darell Gulin/Corbis **Title page:** butterfly ©Darell Gulin/Corbis

Science K–2 Teacher's Guide
ISBN 978-1-60410-719-7

Printed in China.
08 09 10 11 12 13 14 15 16 NP 10 9 8 7 6 5 4 3 2
978-1-60410-719-7

Science K–2
Teacher's Guide Contents

Engage
Concept Poster 1 and Science Vocabulary Cards 1–2 *Whole group activity*

Build Background
Show children side A of card 1 (living thing) and ask them to find a similar image on the poster. (deer, fox, tree, etc.) Place card 1, image side out, in the pocket closest to the image. Say: *The panda is eating a plant called bamboo. What do you eat? The deer is drinking water. What do you drink?* Read the sentence on side A of the card. Repeat with card 2 (nonliving thing).
Ask children the following questions:
- *Which of the things in the picture are living things?*
- *Which of the things are nonliving things?* (rocks, soil, water)
- *Why do you think the snake is watching the frog?* (It eats frogs.)
- *In what ways does the frog move?*
- *Look at the dandelion. How does it change?*

Explore and Learn
Inquiry Activity *Small group activity*

Model the Activity
- Place the materials for Activity Placemat 1 on each table, including copies of Activity Record Sheet 1 (p. 4).
- Model the correct pronunciation for each of the activity materials (Sea-Monkey® eggs, tank with salt water, and hand lens). Have children repeat the words. Explain that Sea-Monkeys® are also called brine shrimp.
- Read the steps of Activity Placemat 1 (Observe Living Things) aloud with children.
- Guide children as they work in small groups to complete the activity and Activity Record Sheet 1. Help children use the hand lens to look at the Sea-Monkey® eggs.
- Have each child work with a partner to complete the **Now Try This** activity.

Discuss the Activity
Invite children to discuss the activity and compare observations. Ask:
- *What did the Sea-Monkey® eggs look like at first?*
- *How did they change?*
- *Are Sea-Monkey® eggs living things? Explain your answer.*
- *How did the temperature of the water affect how quickly they hatched?*

Vocabulary Words
living thing, nonliving thing

Science Objectives
Children will:
- name and classify living and nonliving things
- tell what living things need to change and grow
- observe how Sea-Monkey® eggs change and grow
- explain how warm water affects the speed at which Sea-Monkey® eggs hatch
- interpret and record visual information
- gather and organize materials to complete an activity
- record observations in chart form and interpret those observations

TESOL/LA Objectives
Children will:
- use contextual clues
- follow oral and written directions
- classify objects
- explain changes
- record observations

Materials
- Concept Poster 1
- Science Vocabulary Cards 1–2
- Activity Placemat 1
- Activity Record Sheet 1
- Science Journal
- Science Content Picture Dictionary
- Flip Book Lesson 1
- Concept Web 1
- Radius™ Science Vocabulary Cards 1–2
- Transparency 1
- Lesson Review 1

Vocabulary Word Wall

Place these words on the Word Wall:

living thing, nonliving thing

Have children copy the words in their Science Journals. Next, have children draw a picture to illustrate each word. Photocopy and post the children's illustrations below the appropriate words on the Word Wall.

Cognates

For Spanish-speaking children, it may be helpful to post this cognate chart to show similarities between words in Spanish and English. Keep in mind that children have varying literacy levels in Spanish, and some may not be familiar with these words.

Cognates	
English	Spanish
lens	lente

Science Content Picture Dictionary

For children needing additional help with vocabulary words, refer them to the Science Content Picture Dictionary.

Explain Concepts and Vocabulary
Flip Book *Whole group activity*

Build Background
Review the Concept Poster 1 activity from the **Engage** section. Ask:
- *Which things are living things? How do you know?*
- *Which things are nonliving things? How do you know?*

Read Flip Book, Lesson 1
- Point to the title and read it aloud. Have children repeat the words. Then ask children to brainstorm answers to the title question. If a child uses the words **living thing** or **nonliving thing,** point to the words on the Flip Book page.
- Read the first sentence, pointing to each word as you read. Have children repeat the words. Point to the photo and say: *This is a plant seed. What is happening to the seed?* (The seed is changing and growing into a new plant.) Read the caption and have children repeat the words. Then ask: *Is the seed a living thing?* (yes) *How do you know?* (It changes and grows.)
- Point to the photo of the panda and read the caption. Have children repeat the words. Ask: *Is the panda a living thing?* (yes) *How do you know?* (The panda needs food.) Explain to children that pandas eat a special kind of plant called bamboo.
- Read the second sentence, pointing to each word as you read. Have children repeat the words. Point to the photo of the toy and say: *This is a toy duck. Does the toy move by itself? As time passes, will the toy duck grow and change?* (No, it will not change.) *Is the toy a living thing or a nonliving thing?* (It is a nonliving thing.)
- Point to the photo of the rock and read the caption. Have children repeat the words. Then ask children to tell what living things do, such as eat, drink, grow and change, and breathe. Ask: *Is the rock a living thing or a nonliving thing?* (nonliving) Have children give a reason for their answers.

Make Connections
- Point to the **Make Connections** box and read the question aloud. Then, as a whole group, name the things shown. (pebbles, lion, butterfly, lamp, dog) Ask: *Which of these things are living things?* (lion, butterfly, dog) *Which of these things are nonliving things?* (pebbles, lamp)

Elaborate

Concept Web *Paired activity*

Distribute copies of Concept Web 1 (p. 5). Have each child work with a partner to complete the concept web. For children needing additional help with the web, refer them to the Concept Poster 1, Science Vocabulary Cards 1–2, and the Flip Book. When children have finished, ask volunteers to share and talk about their completed webs.

Radius™ Science Vocabulary Cards
Small group activity

Have children use the Radius™ Audio Learning System and Radius™ Science Vocabulary Cards 1–2 to practice listening to, reading, writing, and speaking each word. Then have children do one or more of the following activities in their Science Journals:

- Provide children with magazines containing pictures of living and nonliving things. Have children cut out and sort the pictures into two groups: *living things* and *nonliving things.* Then have children paste the pictures, by group, in their Science Journals. Tell children to label each group and encourage them to write captions for the pictures.
- Ask children to give examples of living things and nonliving things in their classroom or school. Tell them to write two sentences that name a thing and explain why it is a living or nonliving thing. Write model sentences for children to follow on the board: The book is a _____ thing because _____. Our class pet rabbit is a _____ thing because it _____.
- Invite children to use their own words to write definitions of the vocabulary words. Have them illustrate their definitions.

Evaluate

Transparency 1 *Whole group activity*

Assess Vocabulary Knowledge

Use side B (definition side) of the Science Vocabulary Cards 1–2 to review the lesson vocabulary words. Then distribute a copy of Transparency 1 to each child. Have children cut out the pictures at the bottom of the page and place them in the correct boxes. Model the task for them by using Transparency 1. Invite volunteers to use each vocabulary word in a sentence.

Lesson Review 1 *Individual activity*

Assess Concept Knowledge

Distribute copies of Lesson Review 1 (p. 6). Read the directions aloud and verify children's understanding. For children whose literacy skills are emerging, consider reading the sentences aloud. When children have finished, review the correct answers.

Home Connection
Send the completed copy of Activity Record Sheet 1 (p. 4) home with each child to share with his or her family.

Send a second copy of Transparency 1 home with each child for extra review and practice. Encourage children to work with family members to cut out and place pictures in the appropriate places on the transparency copy. Children can use the transparency copy to review vocabulary words throughout the school year.

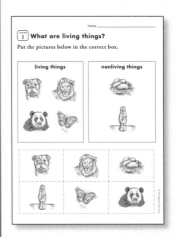

Observe Living Things

1 Record

Look at the Sea-Monkey® eggs with a hand lens.

• Draw what you see.

4 Record

Draw a picture each day to show what you see.

Day	What I saw
1	
2	
3	
4	
5	

5 Share

• Tell what you observed.

_____

_____

• Tell how the Sea-Monkey eggs changed.

_____

_____

Now Try This

Will the Sea-Monkey eggs hatch faster in warmer water? Try it!

Prediction: _____

Results: _____

Note to Parents: Use this sheet to review a science inquiry activity that your child did in class.

Concept Web 1

Fill in the blanks to write the vocabulary words. Draw a picture of each vocabulary word.

___iving ___hing	___onliving thin___

Lesson Review 1

Write the word from the box that completes each sentence.

plant	Living things	rock	Nonliving things

1. _____ grow and change.

2. _____ do not grow and change.

3. A _____ is a living thing.

4. A _____ is a nonliving thing.

What are the parts of a plant?

Engage

Concept Poster 1 and Science Vocabulary
Cards 3–8 *Whole group activity*

Build Background

Show children side A of card 3 (life cycle) and ask them to find a similar image on the poster (the dandelion). Place card 3, image side out, in the pocket closest to the image. Read the sentence on side A of the card. Ask: *How is this plant changing?* (It grows bigger and develops new plant parts.) Repeat with card 4 (seed), card 5 (root), card 6 (stem), card 7 (leaf), and card 8 (flower).

Ask children the following questions:

- *Which of the living things in the picture are plants?*
- *Which part of the plant grows into a new plant?* (seeds)
- *What do plant roots do?* (take in water) *Where do you find the plant roots?* (in soil or water)
- *What job do plant stems do?* (carry water from roots to leaves; hold up the plant)
- *Where is the stem of the tree?* (its woody trunk)
- *What is the job of plant leaves?* (make food for the plant)
- *How do flowers help the plant?* (make the seeds for new plants)

Explore and Learn

Inquiry Activity *Small group activity*

Model the Activity

- Place the materials for Activity Placemat 2 on each table, including copies of Activity Record Sheet 2 (p. 10).
- Model the correct pronunciation for each of the activity materials (tape, scissors, cups, colored water, celery stalk). Have children repeat the words.
- Read the steps of Activity Placemat 2 (Observe Water Move in a Plant) aloud with children.
- Guide children as they work in small groups to complete the activity and Activity Record Sheet 2. Help children understand what it means to predict what will happen to the celery.
- Have each child work with a partner to complete the **Now Try This** activity.

Discuss the Activity

Invite children to discuss the activity and compare observations. Ask:

- *What happened to the celery stalk?*
- *Was your prediction in Step 3 correct? Why or why not?*
- *How can you tell the water reached the top of the celery plant?*
- *What happened when you cut across the top of the celery?*

Vocabulary Words

life cycle, seed, root, stem, leaf, flower

Science Objectives

Children will:

- identify different plant parts
- describe the jobs plant parts do
- sequence events in plant life cycles
- observe how water moves in a plant

TESOL/LA Objectives

Children will:

- construct a chart showing data
- use contextual clues
- predict what will happen in an activity
- follow oral and written directions
- record observations
- explain change

Materials

- Concept Poster 1
- Science Vocabulary Cards 3–8
- Activity Placemat 2
- Activity Record Sheet 2
- Science Journal
- Science Content Picture Dictionary
- Flip Book Lesson 2
- Concept Web 2
- Radius™ Science Vocabulary Cards 3–8
- Transparency 2
- Lesson Review 2

Vocabulary Word Wall
Place these words on the
Word Wall:

**life cycle, seed, root, stem,
leaf, flower**

Have children copy the words in
their Science Journals. Next, have
children draw a picture to illustrate
each word. Photocopy and post
the children's illustrations below
the appropriate words on the
Word Wall.

Cognates

For Spanish-speaking children, it
may be helpful to post this cognate
chart to show similarities between
words in Spanish and English. Keep
in mind that children have varying
literacy levels in Spanish, and
some may not be familiar with
these words.

Cognates	
English	**Spanish**
cycle	ciclo
flower	flor

Science Content Picture Dictionary

For children needing additional
help with vocabulary words, refer
them to the Science Content
Picture Dictionary.

Explain Concepts and Vocabulary
Flip Book *Whole group activity*

Build Background
Review the Concept Poster 1 activity from the **Engage** section. Ask:
- *Which plant parts can you see easily?* (stem, leaves, flowers, seeds)
- *Which plant part is hidden in the soil?* (roots)
- *Which part contains the tiny baby plant?* (seed)

Read Flip Book, Lesson 2
- Point to the title and read it aloud. Have children repeat the words. Then ask children to brainstorm answers to the title question. If a child uses the word **plant** or the names of any of the pictured plant parts, point to the words on the Flip Book page.
- Read the sentence, pointing to each word as you read. Have children repeat the words. Point to the photo at the top right and say: *These are plant seeds. What is the first stage in the plant life cycle?* Read the caption and have children repeat the words. Then ask: *What happens to the seed when it is planted in soil?*
- Point to the next photo and say: *This is the new plant. It is called a seedling.* Read the caption and have children repeat the words. Then ask: *How is the seedling different from the seed?*
- Point to the photo of the adult plant and say: *This is the fully grown plant. It has many different parts.* Read the caption below the arrow and have children repeat the words. Say: *The new plant develops a tiny green shoot and roots. Where do you find plant roots?*
- Point to the plant stem and read the caption. Have children repeat the words. Then ask: *What else does the plant stem do?*
- Point to the leaves and read the caption. Have children repeat the words. Then ask: *Why are the leaves of a plant important?* Finally, point to the flowers and ask: *What part does the grown plant have that the seedling does not?* Read the caption and have children repeat the words. Then ask: *What is the next stage? How is the plant's life cycle like a circle?*

Make Connections
- Point to the **Make Connections** box and read the question aloud. Then, as a whole group, decide which picture comes first, second, third, and last in the plant life cycle. (B, D, A, C)

Elaborate

Concept Web *Paired activity*

Distribute copies of Concept Web 2 (p. 11). Have each child work with a partner to complete the concept web. For children needing additional help with the web, refer them to the Concept Poster 1, Science Vocabulary Cards 3–8, and the Flip Book. When children have finished, ask volunteers to share and talk about their completed webs.

Radius™ Science Vocabulary Cards
Small group activity

Have children use the Radius™ Audio Learning System and Radius™ Science Vocabulary Cards 3–8 to practice listening to, reading, writing, and speaking each word. Then have children do one or more of the following activities in their Science Journals:

- Have children think about a favorite plant. Have them draw a picture of their plant and label all its parts with vocabulary words. Have them write sentences telling what each plant part does.
- Have children pretend they are a seed planted in the ground. Have them work with a partner to draw pictures showing what happens to the seed. Have them write captions to go with the pictures that describe what is happening as they push their roots through the soil, develop a stem, reach their leaves up toward the sunlight, grow flowers, and finally make the seeds.
- Invite children to make a plant alphabet, writing one plant word for each letter. Have children work with a partner to brainstorm plant words that they can use. Encourage them to use vocabulary words as part of their plant alphabets.

Evaluate

Transparency 2 *Whole group activity*

Assess Vocabulary Knowledge

Use side B (definition side) of the Science Vocabulary Cards 3–8 to review the lesson vocabulary words. Then distribute a copy of Transparency 2 to each child. Have children cut out the vocabulary words at the bottom of the page and place them in the correct boxes. Model the task for them by using Transparency 2. Invite volunteers to use each vocabulary word in a sentence.

Lesson Review 2 *Individual activity*

Assess Concept Knowledge

Distribute copies of Lesson Review 2 (p. 12). Read the directions aloud and verify children's understanding. For children whose literacy skills are emerging, consider reading the sentences aloud. When finished, review the correct answers with children.

Home Connection

Send the completed copy of Activity Record Sheet 2 (p. 10) home with each child to share with his or her family.

Send a second copy of Transparency 2 home with each child for extra review and practice. Encourage children to work with family members to cut out and place vocabulary words in the appropriate places on the transparency copy. Children can use the transparency copy to review vocabulary words throughout the school year.

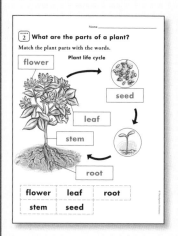

Observe Water Move in a Plant

3 Predict

Write or draw what you think will happen to the celery.

4 Observe and Record

Wait 30 minutes. Look at the celery.

• Draw what you see.

5 Share

• Tell what happened to the water.

_____

_____

• Tell why you think the water moved as it did.

_____

_____

Now Try This

Do the activity again. This time put a cut across a new piece of celery near the leaves. What do you think will happen?

Prediction: _____

Results: _____

Note to Parents: Use this sheet to review a science inquiry activity that your child did in class.

Concept Web 2

Draw pictures to show the life cycle of a plant. Write vocabulary words to name the pictures.

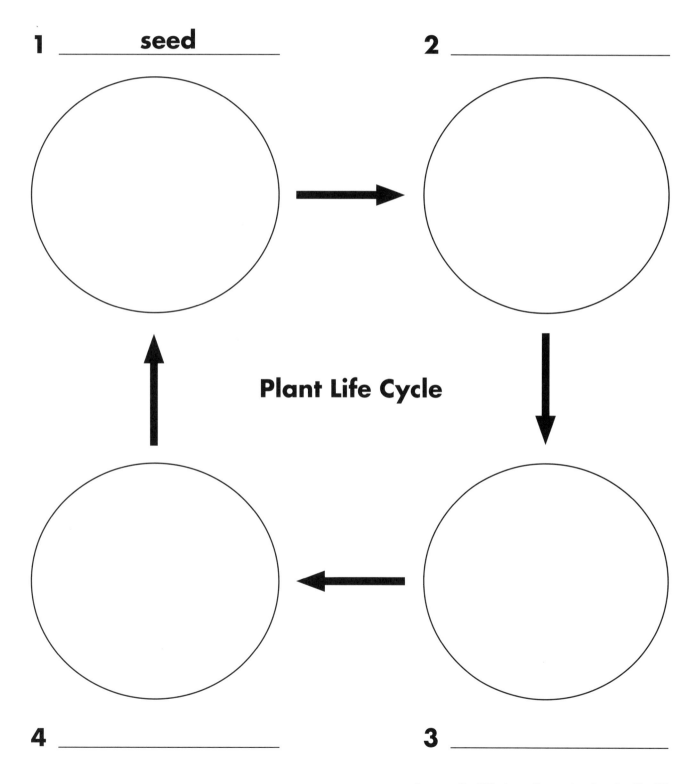

1 _____ **seed** _____

2 _____

Plant Life Cycle

4 _____

3 _____

Lesson Review 2

**Write the word from the box that completes
each sentence.**

flower	leaf	life cycle	root	stem	seed

1. A _____ makes seeds.

2. A _____ takes in water for a plant.

3. A _____ makes food for a plant.

4. A _____ moves water up a plant.

5. Most plants grow from a _____ .

6. A plant grows and changes during its

_____ .

Which animals have a backbone?

Engage

Concept Poster 1 and Science Vocabulary Cards 9–13 *Whole group activity*

Build Background

Show children side A of card 9 (amphibian) and ask them to find a similar image on the poster (frog). Place card 9, image side out, in the pocket closest to the image. Ask: *Where is the frog in the poster?* (in the water) *What kind of animal is a frog?* (amphibian) Read the sentence on side A of the card. Repeat with card 10 (bird), card 11 (reptile), card 12 (fish), and card 13 (mammal).

Ask children the following questions:

- *Where do you see birds in the picture? What are the birds on the log called?*
- *Which animals in the picture are reptiles?* (turtle, snake)
- *Where are the fish in the picture? What are the fish doing?*
- *How many mammals do you see in the picture? What are their names?*
- *Can you find animals that do not have a backbone in the pictures?* (dragonfly, beetle)

Explore and Learn

Inquiry Activity *Small group activity*

Model the Activity

- Place the materials for Activity Placemat 3 on each table, including copies of Activity Record Sheet 3 (p. 16).
- Model the correct pronunciation for each of the activity materials (goggles, chenille stem, clay, beads, cotton squares, tape). Have children repeat the words. Explain that they will make a model of a backbone and of an animal without a backbone.
- Read the steps of Activity Placemat 3 (Model a Backbone) aloud with children.
- Guide children as they work in small groups to complete the activity and Activity Record Sheet 3. Help children to put clay on the end of the chenille stem to keep the beads from falling off.
- Have each child work with a partner to complete the **Now Try This** activity.

Discuss the Activity

Invite children to discuss the activity and compare observations. Ask:

- *You have a backbone. How does it help you move?*
- *What groups of animals have backbones?*
- *A worm is an animal without a backbone. How does a worm move?*

Vocabulary Words

amphibian, bird, reptile, fish, mammal

Science Objectives

Children will:

- identify animals that have backbones
- give examples of animals with backbones
- make a model of a backbone
- tell how a backbone helps an animal move

TESOL/LA Objectives

Children will:

- classify objects
- record observations
- interpret and record visual information
- follow oral and written directions
- analyze, synthesize, and infer from information

Materials

- Concept Poster 1
- Science Vocabulary Cards 9–13
- Activity Placemat 3
- Activity Record Sheet 3
- Science Journal
- Science Content Picture Dictionary
- Flip Book Lesson 3
- Concept Web 3
- Radius™ Science Vocabulary Cards 9–13
- Transparency 3
- Lesson Review 3

Explain Concepts and Vocabulary
Flip Book *Whole group activity*

Vocabulary Word Wall
Place these words on the
Word Wall:

**amphibian, bird, reptile, fish,
mammal**

Have children copy the words in
their Science Journals. Next, have
children draw a picture to illustrate
each word. Post the children's
illustrations below the appropriate
words on the Word Wall.

Cognates
For Spanish-speaking children, it
may be helpful to post this cognate
chart to show similarities between
words in Spanish and English. Keep
in mind that children have varying
literacy levels in Spanish, and
some may not be familiar with
these words.

Cognates	
English	**Spanish**
amphibian	anfibio
reptile	reptil
mammal	mamífero

Science Content Picture Dictionary
For children needing additional
help with vocabulary words, refer
them to the Science Content
Picture Dictionary.

Build Background
Review the Concept Poster 1 activity from the **Engage** section. Ask:
- *Does a fish have a backbone? Does a bird have a backbone?*
- *What are some other kinds of animals that have a backbone?*
- *What are some animals that do not have a backbone?*

Read Flip Book, Lesson 3
- Point to the title and read it aloud. Have children repeat the words.
  Then ask children to brainstorm answers to the title question. If a
  child uses the words **amphibian, bird, reptile, fish,** or **mammal,**
  point to the word on the Flip Book page.
- Read the sentence, pointing to each word as you read. Have children
  repeat the words. Point to the photo of the frog. Say: *This is a frog.*
  Then read the caption and have children repeat the word. Then ask:
  What kind of animal is a frog? (an amphibian) Point to the picture of
  the backbone. Read the caption and have children repeat the word.
  Ask: *Does the frog have a backbone?* (yes)
- Point to the picture of the bird and read the caption. Have children
  repeat the word. Ask: *What kind of animal is this?* (bird) *Does a bird
  have a backbone?* (yes)
- Then point to the picture of the lizard and read the caption. Have
  children repeat the word. Say: *This lizard is an iguana.* Ask: *Does the
  lizard have a backbone?* (yes)
- Next point to the picture of the fish and read the caption. Have
  children repeat the word. Ask: *Does a fish have a backbone?* (yes)
- Finally, point to the picture of the horses and read the caption. Have
  children repeat the word. Ask: *Does a horse have a backbone?* (yes)

Make Connections
- Point to the **Make Connections** box and read the question aloud.
  Then, as a whole group, name the animals shown in the pictures.
  Ask: *What kind of animal is a dog?* (mammal) Repeat with the other
  pictures. Then ask: *How are the animals in the pictures alike?* (All the
  animals have a backbone.)

Elaborate

Concept Web *Paired activity*

Distribute copies of Concept Web 3 (p. 17). Have each child work with a partner to complete the concept web. For children needing additional help with the web, refer them to the Concept Poster 1, Science Vocabulary Cards 9–13, and the Flip Book. When children have finished, ask volunteers to share and talk about their completed webs.

Radius™ Science Vocabulary Cards
Small group activity

Have children use the Radius™ Audio Learning System and Radius™ Science Vocabulary Cards 9–13 to practice listening to, reading, writing, and speaking each word. Then have children do one or more of the following activities in their Science Journals:

- Provide children with nature magazines. Have them cut out or draw a picture that shows an amphibian. Have them write a sentence that tells what kind of animal the picture shows.
- Have children use the same magazines to find and cut out or draw two pictures that show birds. Have them write a sentence that tells how the two birds are alike.
- Have children next find or draw a picture of a reptile. Have them complete the sentence "This ____ is a reptile because it has ____."
- Have children find or draw a picture of a fish. Have them complete the sentence "All fish have a ____ and live in ____."
- Have small groups of children work together to list as many examples of mammals as they can. Then have them write a sentence that tells how all mammals are alike.

Evaluate

Transparency 3 *Whole group activity*

Assess Vocabulary Knowledge

Use side B (definition side) of the Science Vocabulary Cards 9–13 to review the lesson vocabulary words. Then distribute a copy of Transparency 3 to each child. Have children cut out the pictures of animals at the right side of the transparency and place each picture in the correct boxes. Model the task for them by using Transparency 1. Invite volunteers to use each vocabulary word in a sentence.

Lesson Review 3 *Individual activity*

Assess Concept Knowledge

Distribute copies of Lesson Review 3 (p. 18). Read the directions aloud and verify children's understanding. For children whose literacy skills are emerging, consider reading the sentences aloud. When finished, review the correct answers with children.

Home Connection
Send the completed copy of Activity Record Sheet 3 (p. 16) home with each child to share with his or her family.

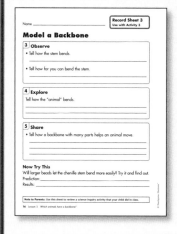

Send a second copy of Transparency 3 home with each child for extra review and practice. Encourage children to work with family members to cut out and place pictures in the appropriate places on the transparency copy. Children can use the transparency copy to review vocabulary words throughout the school year.

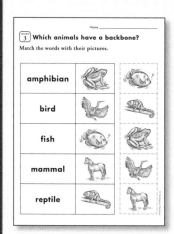

Model a Backbone

3 Observe

- Tell how the stem bends.

  _____

- Tell how far you can bend the stem.

  _____

4 Explore

Tell how the "animal" bends.

_____

_____

5 Share

- Tell how a backbone with many parts helps an animal move.

  _____

  _____

  _____

Now Try This

Will larger beads let the chenille stem bend more easily? Try it and find out.

Prediction:_____

Results: _____

Note to Parents: Use this sheet to review a science inquiry activity that your child did in class.

Concept Web 3

Draw a picture for each kind of animal that has a backbone.

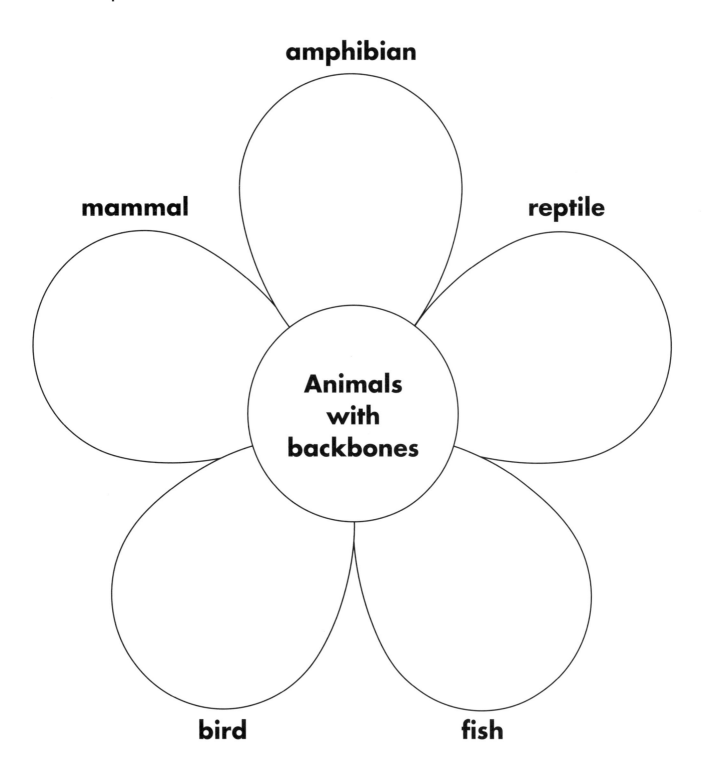

amphibian

mammal

reptile

**Animals
with
backbones**

bird

fish

Lesson Review 3

Circle the names of the animals that have a backbone.

bird   **frog**   **fish**

Draw a picture of each kind of animal.

amphibian	reptile

mammal

How do frogs grow and change?

Engage

Concept Poster 2 and Science Vocabulary Cards 14–16 *Whole group activity*

Build Background

Show children side A of card 14 (life cycle) and ask them to find a similar image on the poster (frog life cycle). Place card 14, image side out, in the pocket closest to the image. Say: *The life cycle of a frog tells about the parts of a frog's life. This cycle has three parts. What are they?* (egg, tadpole, frog) Read the sentence on side A of the card. Repeat with card 15 (egg) and card 16 (tadpole).

Ask children the following questions:
- *What comes first in a frog's life cycle?*
- *What comes last in a frog's life cycle?*
- *Where does the tadpole live? Where does the frog live?*
- *What step comes after the frog grows up?*

Explore and Learn

Inquiry Activity *Small group activity*

Model the Activity

- Place the materials for Activity Placemat 4 on each table, including copies of Activity Record Sheet 4 (p. 22).
- Model the correct pronunciation for each of the activity materials (clay, paper, marker). Have children repeat the words.
- Read the steps of Activity Placemat 4 (Model a Frog Life Cycle) aloud with children.
- Guide children as they work in small groups to complete the activity and Activity Record Sheet 4. Help children use the clay to model a frog or show them an already completed frog.
- Have each child work with a partner to complete the **Now Try This** activity.

Discuss the Activity

Invite children to discuss the activity and compare observations. Ask:
- *What did the egg look like?*
- *How did the egg change to become a tadpole?*
- *How did the tadpole change to become a frog?*
- *What steps in the frog's life cycle did you model?*

Vocabulary Words
life cycle, egg, tadpole

Science Objectives
Children will:
- identify the different stages of a frog's life cycle
- model and describe a frog's life cycle
- interpret and record visual information
- gather and organize materials to complete an activity

TESOL/LA Objectives
Children will:
- use contextual clues
- represent the sequence of events
- analyze, synthesize, and infer from information
- explain change
- write descriptions
- represent information visually

Materials
- Concept Poster 2
- Science Vocabulary Cards 14–16
- Activity Placemat 4
- Activity Record Sheet 4
- Science Journal
- Science Content Picture Dictionary
- Flip Book Lesson 4
- Concept Web 4
- Radius™ Science Vocabulary Cards 14–16
- Transparency 4
- Lesson Review 4

Explain Concepts and Vocabulary
Flip Book *Whole group activity*

Vocabulary Word Wall

Place these words on the Word Wall:

life cycle, egg, tadpole

Have children copy the words in their Science Journals. Next, have children draw a picture to illustrate each word. Photocopy and post the children's illustrations below the appropriate words on the Word Wall.

Cognates

For Spanish-speaking children, it may be helpful to post this cognate chart to show similarities between words in Spanish and English. Keep in mind that children have varying literacy levels in Spanish, and some may not be familiar with these words.

Cognates	
English	Spanish
cycle	ciclo

Science Content Picture Dictionary

For children needing additional help with vocabulary words, refer them to the Science Content Picture Dictionary.

Build Background

Review the Concept Poster 2 activity from the **Engage** section. Ask:

- *What are three steps in a frog's life cycle?*
- *Which comes first, an egg or a tadpole? How do you know?*
- *Which comes last, a frog or a tadpole? How do you know?*

Read Flip Book, Lesson 4

- Point to the title and read it aloud. Have children repeat the words. Then ask children to brainstorm answers to the title question. If a child uses the words **life cycle, egg,** or **tadpole,** point to the words on the Flip Book page.
- Read the sentence, pointing to each word as you read. Have children repeat the words. Point to the photo of the eggs and say: *These are frog eggs. The frog begins its life as an egg.* Read the caption and have children repeat the words. Ask: *What is the first step in the frog's life cycle?* (an egg)
- Point to the photo of the tadpole inside the egg and read the caption. Have children repeat the words. Ask: *Where does a tadpole start to grow?* (in the egg) *How does the tadpole change as it grows?* (The tadpole grows bigger.)
- Point to the photo of the tadpole coming out of the egg and read the caption. Have children repeat the words. Ask: *How does the tadpole change before it comes out of the egg?* (It grows a tail and develops eyes.)
- Point to the photo of the tadpole with legs and read the caption. Have children repeat the words. Ask: *What does a tadpole grow after it leaves the egg?* (legs)
- Point to the photo of the frog and read the caption. Have children repeat the words. Ask: *Where does a grown frog live?* (on land and in water)

Make Connections

- Point to the **Make Connections** box. Then, as a whole group, name the things shown. (egg, tadpole, tadpole with legs, adult frog) Read the captions aloud, and invite children to supply the missing word. Ask: *Which comes first, a frog, a tadpole, or an egg?* (an egg) *Which comes next?* (tadpole) *What does a tadpole grow to turn into a frog?* (legs) *Where does the frog live?* (on land and in water)

Elaborate

Concept Web *Paired activity*

Distribute copies of Concept Web 4 (p. 23). Have each child work with a partner to complete the concept web. For children needing additional help with the web, refer them to the Concept Poster 2, Science Vocabulary Cards 14–16, and the Flip Book. When children have finished, ask volunteers to share and talk about their completed webs.

Radius™ Science Vocabulary Cards
Small group activity

Have children use the Radius™ Audio Learning System and Radius™ Science Vocabulary Cards 14–16 to practice listening to, reading, writing, and speaking each word. Then have children do one or more of the following activities in their Science Journals:

- Have children draw a word web with one of the vocabulary words in the center. Have them add circles with related words. Tell children to use those words to write a sentence about the vocabulary word they chose.
- Have small groups of children brainstorm words to describe frogs such as slippery, bumpy, croaking, jumping, and leaping. Have them draw a picture showing where frogs and tadpoles live. Encourage them to work together to write a four-line poem that describes their picture.
- Have groups of children work together to create a picture book that shows how a frog grows and changes. Have them draw the steps in its life cycle and then write a brief sentence under each picture describing it.

Evaluate

Transparency 4 *Whole group activity*

Assess Vocabulary Knowledge

Use side B (definition side) of the Science Vocabulary Cards 14–16 to review the lesson vocabulary words. Then distribute a copy of Transparency 4 to each child. Have children cut out the pictures at the bottom of the page and place them in the correct circle. Then have them cut out the words and place them in the correct boxes. Model the task for them by using Transparency 4. Invite volunteers to use each vocabulary word in a sentence.

Lesson Review 1 *Individual activity*

Assess Concept Knowledge

Distribute copies of Lesson Review 4 (p. 23). Read the directions aloud and verify children's understanding. For children whose literacy skills are emerging, consider reading the sentences aloud. When finished, review the correct answers with children.

Home Connection
Send the completed copy of Activity Record Sheet 4 (p. 22) home with each child to share with his or her family.

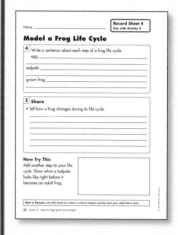

Send a second copy of Transparency 4 home with each child for extra review and practice. Encourage children to work with family members to cut out and place vocabulary words in the appropriate places on the transparency copy. Children can use the transparency copy to review vocabulary words throughout the school year.

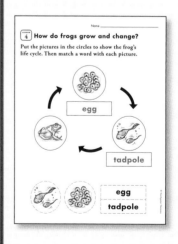

Name ______________________________

Record Sheet 4
Use with Activity 4

Model a Frog Life Cycle

4 Write a sentence about each step of a frog life cycle.

egg ______________________________

____

tadpole ______________________________

____

grown frog ______________________________

____

5 **Share**

- Tell how a frog changes during its life cycle.

____

____

____

____

____

____

Now Try This

Add another step to your life cycle. Show what a tadpole looks like right before it becomes an adult frog.

Note to Parents: Use this sheet to review a science inquiry activity that your child did in class.

Name _____

Concept Web 4

Fill in the blanks to write words describing how a frog grows and changes. Draw a picture of each word.

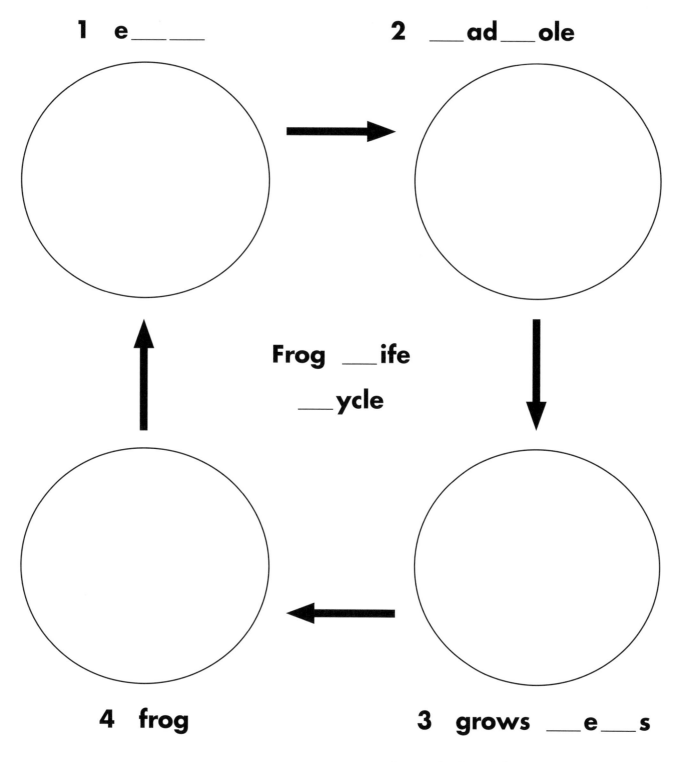

1 e___ ___ ___

2 ___ad___ole

Frog ___ife ___ycle

4 frog

3 grows ___e___s

Lesson Review 4

Draw pictures in the circles to show how a frog grows and changes.

Label each picture with a word from the box.

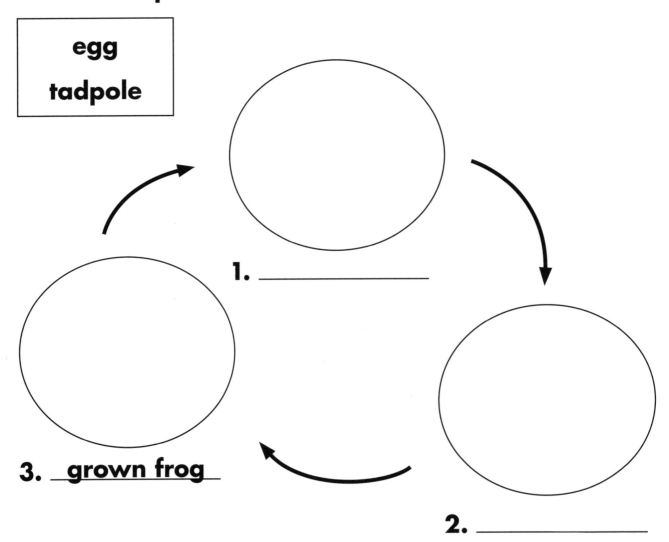

egg

tadpole

1. _____

3. __grown frog__

2. _____

Write words to complete the sentence.

4. The way a frog grows and changes is called a

_____ .

How do butterflies grow and change?

Engage

**Concept Poster 2 and Science Vocabulary
Cards 17–19** *Whole group activity*

Build Background

Show children side A of card 17 (life cycle) and ask them to find a
similar image on the poster (butterfly life cycle). Place card 17, image
side out, in the pocket closest to the image. Say: *This life cycle tells how a
butterfly grows and changes. This cycle has four parts.* Read the sentence on
side A of the card. Repeat with card 18 (larva) and card 19 (pupa).
Ask children the following questions:

- *Which comes first, a larva or an egg?* (egg)
- *Which comes last, a pupa or a grown butterfly?* (butterfly)
- *What happens to the pupa inside the covering?* (It grows and changes.)

Explore and Learn

Inquiry Activity *Small group activity*

Model the Activity

- Place the materials for Activity Placemat 5 on each table, including
  copies of Activity Record Sheet 5 (p. 28).
- Model the correct pronunciation for each of the activity materials
  (paper squares, crayons, scissors, clay). Have children repeat the
  words.
- Read the steps of Activity Placemat 5 (Model a Butterfly Life Cycle)
  aloud with children.
- Guide children as they work in small groups to complete the activity
  and Activity Record Sheet 5. Help children cut paper to make wings
  and use clay and paper to model an egg, larva, pupa, and butterfly.
- Have each child work with a partner to complete the **Now Try This**
  activity.

Discuss the Activity

Invite children to discuss the activity and compare observations. Ask:

- *What did the egg look like?*
- *How did the egg change to become a larva?*
- *How does the butterfly look when it comes out of the pupa?*
- *Do any steps in the butterfly's life cycle look alike?*

Vocabulary Words
life cycle, larva, pupa

Science Objectives
Children will:
- identify the stages of a
  butterfly's life cycle
- model and describe a butterfly's
  life cycle
- interpret and record visual
  information
- gather and organize materials
  to complete an activity

TESOL/LA Objectives
Children will:
- follow oral and written directions
- select, connect, and explain
  information
- represent information visually
- understand and produce
  technical vocabulary
- connect new information to
  information previously learned

Materials
- Concept Poster 2
- Science Vocabulary Cards 17–19
- Activity Placemat 5
- Activity Record Sheet 5
- Science Journal
- Science Content Picture
  Dictionary
- Flip Book Lesson 5
- Concept Web 5
- Radius™ Science Vocabulary
  Cards 17–19
- Transparency 5
- Lesson Review 5

Vocabulary Word Wall

Place these words on the Word Wall:

life cycle, larva, pupa

Have children copy the words in their Science Journals. Next, have children draw a picture to illustrate each word. Photocopy and post the children's illustrations below the appropriate words on the Word Wall.

Cognates

For Spanish-speaking children, it may be helpful to post this cognate chart to show similarities between words in Spanish and English. Keep in mind that children have varying literacy levels in Spanish, and some may not be familiar with these words.

Cognates	
English	Spanish
cycle	ciclo
larva	larva

Science Content Picture Dictionary

For children needing additional help with vocabulary words, refer them to the Science Content Picture Dictionary.

Explain Concepts and Vocabulary

Flip Book *Whole group activity*

Build Background

Review the Concept Poster 2 activity from the **Engage** section. Ask:
- *What are four parts of a butterfly's life cycle?*
- *Which comes first, an egg or a larva? How do you know?*
- *Which comes last, a butterfly or a pupa? How do you know?*

Read Flip Book, Lesson 5

- Point to the title and read it aloud. Have children repeat the words. Then ask children to brainstorm answers to the title question. If a child uses the words **life cycle, egg, larva,** or **pupa** point to the words on the Flip Book page.
- Read the first sentence, pointing to each word as you read. Have children repeat the words. Point to the photo of the butterfly and read the caption. Have children repeat the words. Say: *A grown butterfly has wings.*
- Read the second sentence. Point to the photo of the egg and say: *This is a butterfly egg. What will happen to it?* (It will grow and change into a butterfly.) Read the caption and have children repeat the words. Then ask: *What is the first part of the butterfly's life cycle?* (an egg) *How do you know?* (A butterfly begins as an egg.)
- Point to the photo of the larva and read the caption. Have children repeat the words. Ask: *Where does a larva come from?* (the egg) *How is the larva different from the egg?* (The egg is round; the larva is long and has many legs.) *What else is a butterfly larva called?* (a caterpillar) Point to the photos of the pupa and read the caption. Have children repeat the words. Ask: *What comes first, a caterpillar or a pupa?* (a caterpillar) *How is the pupa different from the larva?* (The pupa is inside a covering.) *What happens to the pupa inside the covering?* (It changes.)
- Point to the photo of the butterfly coming out of the covering and read the caption. Have children repeat the words. Ask: *What did the pupa change into inside the covering?* (a grown butterfly) *When did the butterfly change from a larva?* (when it was a pupa) *What does a grown butterfly have after it comes out of the covering?* (wings)

Make Connections

- Point to the **Make Connections** box and read the directions aloud. Then, as a whole group, name the things shown. (pupa, butterfly, egg, larva, or caterpillar) Ask: *Which picture comes first, a butterfly, a larva, a pupa, or an egg?* (an egg; C) *Which comes next?* (larva; D) *What comes after the larva?* (pupa; A) *What picture comes last?* (grown butterfly with wings; B)

Elaborate

Concept Web *Paired activity*

Distribute copies of Concept Web 5 (p. 29). Have each child work with a partner to complete the concept web. For children needing additional help with the web, refer them to the Concept Poster 2, Science Vocabulary Cards 17–19, and the Flip Book. When children have finished, ask volunteers to share and talk about their completed webs.

Radius™ Science Vocabulary Cards
Small group activity

Have children use the Radius™ Audio Learning System and Radius™ Science Vocabulary Cards 17–19 to practice listening to, reading, writing, and speaking each word. Then have children do one or more of the following activities in their Science Journals:

- Tell children that moths have a four-step life cycle like butterflies. Have children draw and label pictures of the moth life cycle and paste them into their Science Journals. Encourage children to compare the insect life cycle to the frog life cycle they learned about in Lesson 4.
- Provide children with magazines that include photos of different insects. Have them make a collage of insect photos in their Science Journal and then write a sentence that describes how they are alike.
- Invite children to use their own words to write definitions of the vocabulary words. Have them illustrate their definitions.

Evaluate

Transparency 5 *Whole group activity*

Assess Vocabulary Knowledge

Use side B (definition side) of the Science Vocabulary Cards 17–19 to review the lesson vocabulary words. Then distribute a copy of Transparency 5 to each child. Have children cut out the pictures at the bottom of the page and place them in the correct squares. Model the task for them by using Transparency 5. Invite volunteers to use each vocabulary word in a sentence.

Lesson Review 5 *Individual activity*

Assess Concept Knowledge

Distribute copies of Lesson Review 5 (p. 30). Read the directions aloud and verify children's understanding. For children whose literacy skills are emerging, consider reading the sentences aloud. When finished, review the correct answers with children.

Home Connection

Send the completed copy of Activity Record Sheet 5 (p. 28) home with each child to share with his or her family.

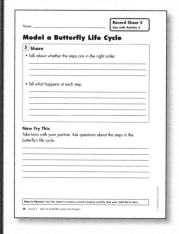

Send a second copy of Transparency 5 home with each child for extra review and practice. Encourage children to work with family members to cut out and place pictures in the appropriate places on the transparency copy. Children can use the transparency copy to review vocabulary words throughout the school year.

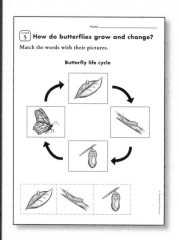

Name ______________________

Record Sheet 5
Use with Activity 5

Model a Butterfly Life Cycle

5 Share

- Talk about whether the steps are in the right order.

- Tell what happens at each step.

Now Try This

Take turns with your partner. Ask questions about the steps in the butterfly's life cycle.

Note to Parents: Use this sheet to review a science inquiry activity that your child did in class.

Concept Web 5

Fill in the blanks to write the vocabulary words. Draw a picture of each vocabulary word.

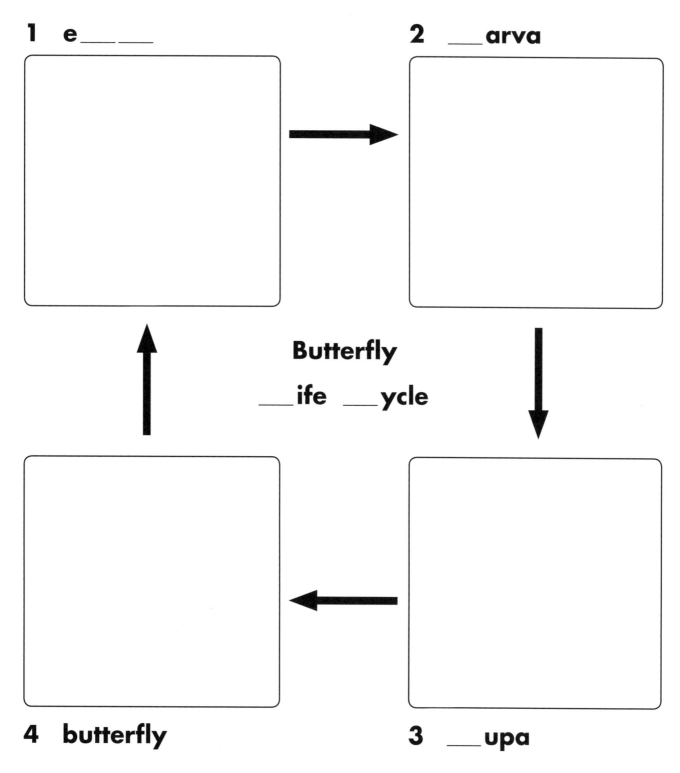

1 e__ __ __

2 __arva

Butterfly

__ife __ycle

4 butterfly

3 __upa

Lesson Review 5

Write the word from the box that completes each sentence.

pupa	larva	life cycle

1. A butterfly grows and changes in a

_____ .

2. A caterpillar is a butterfly _____ .

3. A caterpillar changes to a _____ .

How do mammals grow and change?

Engage

Concept Poster 2 and Science Vocabulary
Card 20 *Whole group activity*

Build Background

Show children side A of card 20 (life cycle) and ask them to find a similar image on the poster (the rabbit life cycle). Place card 20, image side out, in the pocket closest to the image. Say: *This life cycle tells how a rabbit grows and changes. What kind of animal is a rabbit?* (mammal) Read the sentence on side A of the card.

Ask children the following questions:

* *How is the baby different from a full grown rabbit?* (hairless, tiny, mother feeds it milk)
* *What is the difference between the young rabbits and the baby rabbits?* (larger, can feed itself plants)
* *What are the stages in a rabbit's life called?* (its life cycle)

Explore and Learn

Inquiry Activity *Small group activity*

Model the Activity

* Place the materials for Activity Placemat 6 on each table, including copies of Activity Record Sheet 6 (p. 34).
* Model the correct pronunciation for each of the activity materials (thermometers, cloth, cotton balls, plastic bags, pan of ice water). Have children repeat the words.
* Read the steps of Activity Placemat 6 (Explore How Mammals Stay Warm) aloud with children.
* Guide children as they work in small groups to complete the activity and Activity Record Sheet 6. Help children package the thermometers in the bags, time the waiting period, and read the thermometers.
* Have each child work with a partner to complete the **Now Try This** activity.

Discuss the Activity

Invite children to discuss the activity and compare observations. Ask:

* *Which thermometer had the lower temperature?*
* *Which bag kept the thermometer warmer?*
* *How are the cotton balls like a mammal's fur?*
* *If you were outside in the cold, would you like to have fur or something similar covering your skin? Why?*

Vocabulary Word
life cycle

Science Objectives
Children will:

* identify the stages of a mammal's life cycle
* model how fur keeps mammals warm
* interpret and record visual information
* compare and contrast
* test a hypothesis

TESOL/LA Objectives
Children will:

* make pictures to check comprehension of a process
* follow oral and written directions
* participate in full class, group, and pair discussions
* hypothesize and predict
* interpret information presented visually
* use contextual clues

Materials

* Concept Poster 2
* Science Vocabulary Card 20
* Activity Placemat 6
* Activity Record Sheet 6
* Science Journal
* Science Content Picture Dictionary
* Flip Book Lesson 6
* Concept Web 6
* Radius™ Science Vocabulary Card 20
* Transparency 6
* Lesson Review 6

Explain Concepts and Vocabulary

Flip Book *Whole group activity*

Build Background

Review the Concept Poster 2 activity from the **Engage** section. Ask:
- *What are the three parts of the rabbit's life cycle?*
- *How is the baby rabbit different from the young rabbit?*
- *How is the young rabbit different from the grown rabbit?*

Read Flip Book, Lesson 6

- Point to the title and read it aloud. Have children repeat the words. Then ask children to brainstorm answers to the title question. If a child uses the term **life cycle,** point to the words on the Flip Book page.
- Read the first sentence, pointing to each word as you read. Have children repeat the words. Point to the photo of the baby bunnies. Read the caption and have children repeat the words. Then ask: *What do baby bunnies eat?* (They drink milk from their mother.) *Where do the baby bunnies live?* (in a nest)
- Point to the photo of the young rabbit and read the caption. Have children repeat the words. Ask: *What happens to a bunny?* (It grows and learns to do many things. It can find its own food.)
- Read the second sentence, pointing to each word as you read. Point to the photo of the adult rabbit and read the caption. Have children repeat the words. Say: *This is a grown rabbit. It is a mammal. What are some other mammals?* (dogs, cats, mice, hamsters) Ask: *What comes first, a bunny or a rabbit?* (a bunny) *How do you know?* (The bunny has to grow and change to become a grown rabbit.)
- Point again to the photos of the grown rabbit and the baby bunnies. Ask: *What are the three parts of a rabbit's life cycle?* (baby, bunny, grown rabbit)

Make Connections

- Point to the **Make Connections** box and read the direction line aloud. Then, as a whole group, name the things shown. (young bunnies, grown rabbit, baby rabbits) Ask: *Which picture comes first, a rabbit, bunnies, or baby bunnies?* (C; the baby bunnies) *Which picture comes next?* (A; the bunnies) *What picture comes last?* (B; the grown rabbit) *What can a grown rabbit do?* (have bunnies of its own)

Elaborate

Concept Web *Paired activity*

Distribute copies of Concept Web 6 (p. 35). Have each child work with a partner to complete the concept web. For children needing additional help with the web, refer them to the Concept Poster 2, Science Vocabulary Card 20, and the Flip Book. When children have finished, ask volunteers to share and talk about their completed webs.

Radius™ Science Vocabulary Card
Small group activity

Have children use the Radius™ Audio Learning System and Radius™ Science Vocabulary Card 20 to practice listening to, reading, writing, and speaking each word. Then have children do one or more of the following activities in their Science Journals:

- Have children draw and label pictures of the mammal life cycle and paste them into their Science Journals. Encourage children to compare the mammal life cycle to the other life cycles they learned in Lessons 4 and 5.

- Provide children with magazines that include photos of young and grown mammals. Have them cut out and sort the pictures into two groups: *young mammals* and *grown mammals.* (If pictures of newborn or baby mammals are available, have children sort into three groups: *baby mammals, young mammals,* and *grown mammals.*) Then have children paste the pictures, by group, into their Science Journals. Guide children to label each group, and encourage them to write captions for their pictures.

- Invite children to use their own words to write a definition of the vocabulary word. Have them illustrate their definition.

Evaluate

Transparency 6 *Whole group activity*

Assess Vocabulary Knowledge

Use side B (definition side) of the Science Vocabulary Card 20 to review the lesson vocabulary word. Then distribute a copy of Transparency 6 to each child. Have children cut out the vocabulary word and the numbers at the bottom of the page, then have them place each in the correct square. Model the task for them by using Transparency 6. Invite a volunteer to use the vocabulary word in a sentence.

Lesson Review 6 *Individual activity*

Assess Concept Knowledge

Distribute copies of Lesson Review 6 (p. 36). Read the directions aloud and verify children's understanding. For children whose literacy skills are emerging, consider reading the sentences aloud. When finished, review the correct answers with children.

Home Connection
Send the completed copy of Activity Record Sheet 6 (p. 34) home with each child to share with his or her family.

Send a second copy of Transparency 6 home with each child for extra review and practice. Encourage children to work with family members to cut out and place the vocabulary word and the numbers in the appropriate places on the transparency copy. Children can use the transparency copy to review vocabulary words throughout the school year.

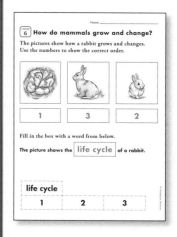

Explore How Mammals Stay Warm

5 Record and Share

Draw thermometers to show the temperature in each plastic bag.

Covered thermometer	Uncovered thermometer

• Tell how the cotton and cloth is like fur on a mammal.

_____

_____

Now Try This

Will more fur keep a mammal warmer? Use more cotton balls to find out.

Prediction: _____

Results: _____

Note to Parents: Use this sheet to review a science inquiry activity that your child did in class.

Concept Web 6

Fill in the blanks to write the vocabulary word. Draw each picture in the rabbit life cycle.

The rabbit grows and changes during its ___ife ___ycle.

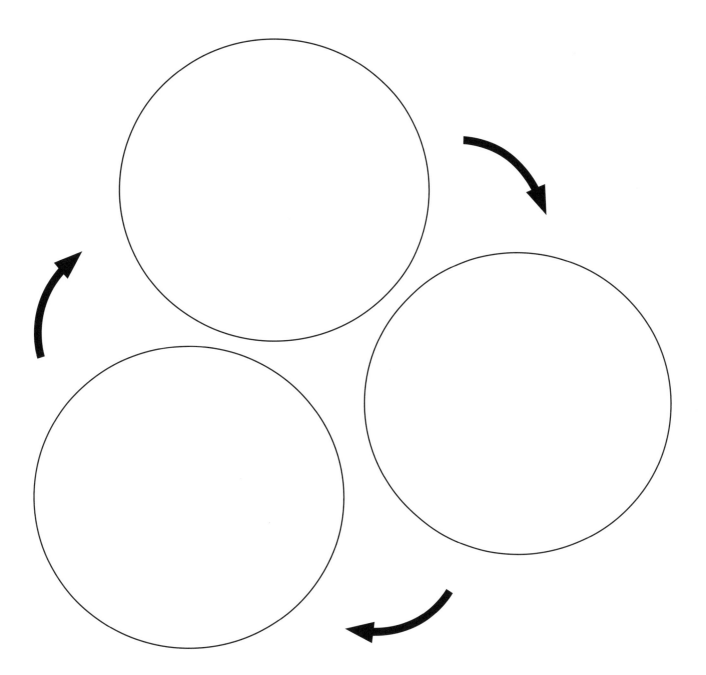

Lesson Review 6

Write a word from the box that completes each sentence.

First	Next	life cycle	Last

1. _____ the bunny becomes

a grown rabbit.

2. _____ the bunny can find

its own food.

3. _____ a bunny drinks milk

from its mother.

4. A rabbit grows and changes during

its _____ .

Where do plants and animals live?

Engage

Concept Poster 3 and Science Vocabulary
Cards 21–25 *Whole group activity*

Build Background

Show children side A of card 21 (environment) and ask them to find a similar image on the poster. (desert) Place card 21, image side out, in the pocket closest to the image. Say: *This picture shows a desert environment. Can you name another kind of environment?* (ocean) Read the sentence on side A of the card. Repeat with card 22 (habitat), card 23 (adaptation), card 24 (camouflage), and card 25 (shelter).

Ask children the following questions:
- *What is the cactus's habitat? What is the shark's habitat?*
- *How do the eagle's wings help it live in its habitat?*
- *Why is the scorpion difficult to see?*
- *What is one place that an animal finds shelter?*
- *Find the octopus. Why is it hard to see?*

Explore and Learn

Inquiry Activity *Small group activity*

Model the Activity

- Place the materials for Activity Placemat 7 on each table, including copies of Activity Record Sheet 7 (p. 40).
- Model the correct pronunciation for each of the activity materials (green paper, scissors, water, wax paper). Have children repeat the words. Explain that children should make their two leaf shapes the same size.
- Read the steps of Activity Placemat 7 (Explore How Plants Keep Water) aloud with children.
- Guide children as they work in small groups to complete the activity and Activity Record Sheet 7. Help children use the spray bottle to wet both leaf shapes equally.
- Have each child work with a partner to complete the **Now Try This** activity.

Discuss the Activity

Invite children to discuss the activity and compare observations. Ask:
- *Which leaf took the longest time to dry?*
- *Why did the covered leaf shape take longer to dry?*
- *Why do you think a wax coating on a plant's leaves would help keep the leaves from drying out?*
- *How did the size of the leaf shape in waxed paper affect how fast it dried?*

Vocabulary Words
environment, habitat, adaptation, camouflage, shelter

Science Objectives
Children will:
- name examples of habitats
- describe adaptations of living things
- explain what camouflage is
- describe examples of shelter
- explore how plants keep water
- infer how a wax coating keeps plants from drying out

TESOL/LA Objectives
Children will:
- retell information
- use contextual clues
- compare objects
- explain change
- record observations
- make pictures to show comprehension
- follow oral and written directions

Materials
- Concept Poster 3
- Science Vocabulary Cards 21–25
- Activity Placemat 7
- Activity Record Sheet 7
- Science Journal
- Science Content Picture Dictionary
- Flip Book Lesson 7
- Concept Web 7
- Radius™ Science Vocabulary Cards 21–25
- Transparency 7
- Lesson Review 7

Vocabulary Word Wall

Place these words on the Word Wall:

environment, habitat, adaptation, camouflage, shelter

Have children copy the words in their Science Journals. Next, have children draw a picture to illustrate each word. Photocopy and post the children's illustrations below the appropriate words on the Word Wall.

Cognates

For Spanish-speaking children, it may be helpful to post this cognate chart to show similarities between words in Spanish and English. Keep in mind that children have varying literacy levels in Spanish, and some may not be familiar with these words.

Cognates	
English	**Spanish**
adaptation	adaptación
habitat	hábitat

Science Content Picture Dictionary

For children needing additional help with vocabulary words, refer them to the Science Content Picture Dictionary.

Explain Concepts and Vocabulary

Flip Book *Whole group activity*

Build Background

Review the Concept Poster 3 activity from the **Engage** section. Ask:
- *What are two kinds of environments?*
- *Can you name a plant or animal and tell what its habitat is?*
- *What is an adaptation that an eagle has?*
- *Why is it hard to see some animals in their habitats?*
- *Where does the eel find shelter?* (inside a sponge)

Read Flip Book, Lesson 7

- Point to the title and read it aloud. Have children repeat the words. Then ask children to brainstorm answers to the title question. If a child uses the word **environment** or any other vocabulary word, point to the word on the Flip Book page.
- Read the first sentence, pointing to each word as you read. Have children repeat the words. Point to the background photo and say: *This is a forest environment. What are some things that live in the forest?* (trees, ferns, mushrooms, raccoons) Point to the mushroom photo. Read the caption and have children repeat the words. Then ask: *What is the habitat of the mushroom?* (a tree)
- Point to the photo of the birds and read the caption. Have children repeat the words. Ask: *What is an adaptation these birds have?* (the way they fly in a pattern) Point to the photo of the bat and read the caption. Have children repeat the words. Ask: *How do the bat's wings help it live?* (Wings let the bat fly to hunt food.)
- Point to the photo of the insect and say: *Find the insect on the leaf.* Read the caption, pointing to each word as you read. Have children repeat the words. *Why is it hard to see the insect?* (Its color matches the leaf.)
- Point to the photo of the raccoon and read the caption. Have children repeat the words. Ask: *Where is the raccoon?* (in a hole in the tree) *What does the raccoon use the hole for?* (shelter)

Make Connections

- Point to the **Make Connections** box and read the question aloud. Then, as a whole group, name the things shown. (eel in a sponge, fish, bat) Ask: *What sentence could you say that tells about the eel?* (The eel finds shelter in the sponge.) *What sentence could you say that tells about the fish?* (The fish uses camouflage to hide in the pond plants.) *What sentence could you say that tells about the bat?* (The bat's wings are an adaptation that lets it fly.)

Elaborate

Concept Web *Paired activity*

Distribute copies of Concept Web 7 (p. 41). Have each child work with a partner to complete the concept web. For children needing additional help with the web, refer them to the Concept Poster 3, Science Vocabulary Cards 21–25, and the Flip Book. When children have finished, ask volunteers to share and talk about their completed webs.

Radius™ Science Vocabulary Cards
Small group activity

Have children use the Radius™ Audio Learning System and Radius™ Science Vocabulary Cards 21–25 to practice listening to, reading, writing, and speaking each word. Then have children do one or more of the following activities in their Science Journals:

- Provide children with magazines containing pictures of different environments. Have children cut out a picture of one environment and paste the picture in their Science Journals. Tell children to write a sentence that tells what kind of environment is shown.
- Ask children to draw or find pictures in magazines that illustrate a living thing's habitat, an adaptation of a living thing, an animal that uses camouflage, and an animal using shelter. Tell them to write a sentence that tells about each picture. Write model sentences for children to follow on the board: The _____ is the _____'s habitat. The _____ of a _____ is an adaptation. A _____ uses camouflage to hide in the _____. A _____ finds shelter in the _____.
- Invite children to use their own words to write definitions of the vocabulary words. Have them illustrate their definitions.

Evaluate

Transparency 7 *Whole group activity*

Assess Vocabulary Knowledge

Use side B (definition side) of the Science Vocabulary Cards 21–25 to review the lesson vocabulary words. Then distribute a copy of Transparency 7 to each child. Have children cut out the vocabulary words at the bottom of the page and place them in the correct boxes. Model the task for them by using Transparency 7. Invite volunteers to read each sentence.

Lesson Review 7 *Individual activity*

Assess Concept Knowledge

Distribute copies of Lesson Review 7 (p. 42). Read the directions aloud and verify children's understanding. For children whose literacy skills are emerging, consider reading the sentences aloud. When finished, review the correct answers with children.

Home Connection
Send the completed copy of Activity Record Sheet 7 (p. 40) home with each child to share with his or her family.

Send a second copy of Transparency 7 home with each child for extra review and practice. Encourage children to work with family members to cut out and place vocabulary words in the appropriate places on the transparency copy. Children can use the transparency copy to review vocabulary words throughout the school year.

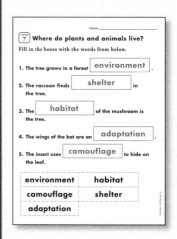

Explore How Plants Keep Water

4 Record

- Write the time it takes for the leaf shapes to dry.

Leaf shape	Amount of time to dry
without wax paper	
with wax paper	

5 Share

- Tell why a desert plant might have a wax covering on its leaves.

_____

_____

_____

Now Try This

Test a large leaf and a small leaf in wax paper.
Which dries faster?

_____

Note to Parents: Use this sheet to review a science inquiry activity that your child did in class.

Concept Web 7

Draw a picture of each vocabulary word.

environment	
habitat	**adaptation**
camouflage	**shelter**

Lesson Review 7

Circle the word to complete each sentence.

1. The wings of a bat are _____ .

an adaptation　　　**a habitat**

2. A raccoon finds _____ in a tree.

camouflage　　　**shelter**

3. The place where an animal lives is its _____ .

camouflage　　　**habitat**

4. A forest is one kind of _____ .

adaptation　　　**environment**

5. An insect uses _____ to hide on a leaf.

an environment　　　**camouflage**

How do living things get food?

Engage

Concept Poster 3 and Science Vocabulary Cards 26–32 *Whole group activity*

Build Background

Show children side A of card 26 (food) and ask them to find a similar image on the poster. (rabbit) Place card 26, image side out, in the pocket closest to the image. Say: *This picture shows a flower. Can you name the animal that eats the flower?* (turtle) *Can you name an animal on the poster that would eat the rabbit?* (coyote) Read the sentence on side A of the card. Repeat with card 27 (food chain), card 28 (food web), card 29 (prey), card 30 (predator), card 31 (producer), and card 32 (consumer). Ask children the following questions:

* *What is the turtle's food? What is the alligator's food?*
* *How can you make a food chain from the living things on the poster?*
* *How many living things are in the food web? What are they?*
* *What is prey for the frog? What might be prey for the shark?*
* *What is the alligator? What predators do you see in the poster?*
* *What is the water lily? Can you name a producer on the poster?*
* *What is the turtle? Can you name a consumer on the poster?*

Explore and Learn

Inquiry Activity *Small group activity*

Model the Activity

* Place the materials for Activity Placemat 8 on each table, including copies of Activity Record Sheet 8 (p. 46).
* Model the correct pronunciation for each of the activity materials (paper, crayons, tape, yarn). Have children repeat the words. Explain that they will model a food web to show what living things eat to get energy.
* Read the steps of Activity Placemat 8 (Model a Food Web) aloud with children.
* Guide children as they work in small groups to complete the activity and Activity Record Sheet 8. Help children figure out which living thing eats which other living thing.
* Have two groups work together to complete the **Now Try This** activity.

Discuss the Activity

Invite children to discuss the activity and compare observations. Ask:
* *How many living things were in your food web?*
* *Do some animals eat more than one other kind of animal?*
* *How do plants get food?*
* *How many living things were in the food web in the **Now Try This?***

Vocabulary Words
food, food chain, food web, prey, predator, producer, consumer

Science Objectives
Children will:
* tell what a food chain is and give an example
* distinguish between predators and prey
* distinguish between producers and consumers
* model a food web

TESOL/LA Objectives
Children will:
* retell information
* use contextual clues
* compare objects
* classify objects
* record observations
* make pictures to show comprehension
* follow oral and written directions

Materials
* Concept Poster 3
* Science Vocabulary Cards 26–32
* Activity Placemat 8
* Activity Record Sheet 8
* Science Journal
* Science Content Picture Dictionary
* Flip Book Lesson 8
* Concept Web 8
* Radius™ Science Vocabulary Cards 26–32
* Transparency 8
* Lesson Review 8

Vocabulary Word Wall

Place these words on the Word Wall:

food, food chain, food web, prey, predator, producer, consumer

Have children copy the words in their Science Journals. Next, have children draw a picture to illustrate each word. Post the children's illustrations below the appropriate words on the Word Wall.

Cognates

For Spanish-speaking children, it may be helpful to post this cognate chart to show similarities between words in Spanish and English. Keep in mind that children have varying literacy levels in Spanish, and some may not be familiar with these words.

Cognates	
English	**Spanish**
predator	depredador
producer	productor

Science Content Picture Dictionary

For children needing additional help with vocabulary words, refer them to the Science Content Picture Dictionary.

Explain Concepts and Vocabulary
Flip Book *Whole group activity*

Build Background

Review the Concept Poster 3 activity from the **Engage** section. Ask:
- *What are two examples of producers?*
- *What are two examples of consumers?*
- *What is an example of a predator and its prey?*
- *What living things make up a food chain?*
- *What food chains make up a food web?*

Read Flip Book, Lesson 8

- Point to the title and read it aloud. Have children repeat the words. Then ask children to brainstorm answers to the title question. If a child uses the word **food** or any other vocabulary word, point to the word on the Flip Book page.
- Read the first sentence, pointing to each word as you read. Have children repeat the words. Point to the background scene and say: *This is a swamp. What are some things that live there?* (water lilies, insects, alligators, frogs, snakes, turtles)
- Read the second sentence, pointing to each word as you read. Have children repeat the words. Ask: *How do the animals in the swamp get energy?* (from food) *What shows how they get energy?* (food chains) Point to the frog and snake photos. Read the caption and have children repeat the words. Then ask: *Does the frog eat the snake or does the snake eat the frog?* (snake eats frog) *Which animal is the prey?* (frog)
- Read the third sentence, pointing to each word as you read. Have children repeat the words. Ask: *What makes up the food web in the swamp?* (all the food chains in the swamp) Point to the photo of the alligator and read the caption. Have children repeat the words. Ask: *What is the alligator called? Why?* (a predator; it eats other animals)
- Point to the photo of the water lily and say: *This water lily can make its own food.* Read the caption, pointing to each word as you read. Have children repeat the words. Ask: *What is the water lily called?* (a producer)
- Point to the photo of the turtle and read the caption. Have children repeat the words. Ask: *Why is the turtle a consumer?* (It eats food for energy.) *What other consumers do you see?* (frog, snake, alligator, dragonfly)

Make Connections

- Point to the **Make Connections** box and read the captions aloud. Then, as a whole group, name the things shown. (bird eating a fish, turtle eating a plant) Ask: *In the first picture, what is the bird?* (predator) *What is the fish?* (prey) *In the second picture, what is the turtle?* (consumer) *What is the plant?* (producer)

Elaborate

Concept Web *Paired activity*

Distribute copies of Concept Web 8 (p. 47). Have each child work with a partner to complete the concept web. For children needing additional help with the web, refer them to the Concept Poster 3, Science Vocabulary Cards 26–32, and the Flip Book. When children have finished, ask volunteers to share and talk about their completed webs.

Radius™ Science Vocabulary Cards

Small group activity

Have children use the Radius™ Audio Learning System and Radius™ Science Vocabulary Cards 26–32 to practice listening to, reading, writing, and speaking each word. Then have children do one or more of the following activities in their Science Journals:

- Provide nature magazines with pictures of different living things. Have children cut out pictures and put them together to make a food chain or a web. Then have children paste the pictures in their Science Journals and write a sentence that tells where it would be found.

- Ask children to draw or find pictures in magazines that illustrate different living things. Have children work with a partner to write one or more sentences using a vocabulary word to tell about each picture. Write these model sentences for children to follow: The _____ is a predator/prey because _____. The _____ is a producer/consumer because _____.

- Invite children to use their own words to write definitions of the vocabulary words. Have them illustrate their definitions.

Evaluate

Transparency 8 *Whole group activity*

Assess Vocabulary Knowledge

Use side B (definition side) of the Science Vocabulary Cards 26–32 to review the lesson vocabulary words. Then distribute a copy of Transparency 8 to each child. Have children cut out the words at the bottom of the page and place them in the correct boxes. Model the task for them by using Transparency 8. Invite volunteers to use each vocabulary word in a sentence.

Lesson Review 8 *Individual activity*

Assess Concept Knowledge

Distribute copies of Lesson Review 8 (p. 48). Read the directions aloud and verify children's understanding. For children whose literacy skills are emerging, consider reading the sentences aloud. When finished, review the correct answers with children.

Home Connection
Send the completed copy of Activity Record Sheet 8 (p. 46) home with each child to share with his or her family.

Send a second copy of Transparency 8 home with each child for extra review and practice. Encourage children to work with family members to cut out and place vocabulary words in the appropriate places on the transparency copy. Children can use the transparency copy to review vocabulary words throughout the school year.

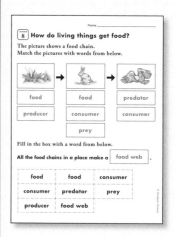

Model a Food Web

5 Record and Share

Draw your food web.

• Tell how the living things in the food web are connected.

_____

_____

_____

Now Try This

What would your food web look like if you joined with another group?
Do it!

Prediction: _____

_____

Results: _____

_____

Note to Parents: Use this sheet to review a science inquiry activity that your child did in class.

© Northpoint Horizons™

Concept Web 8

Draw a picture of each word in the boxes below.

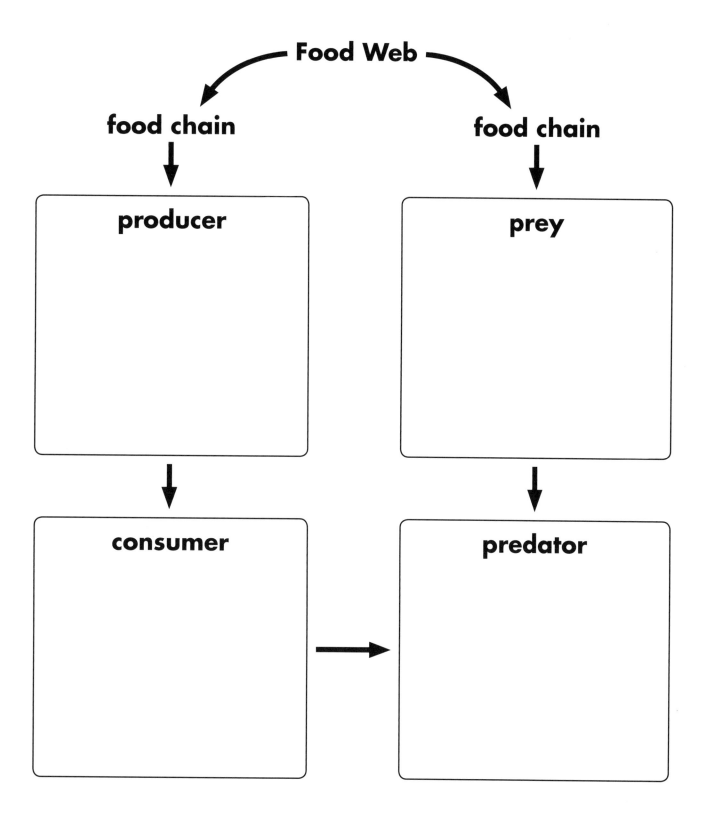

Food Web

food chain   food chain

producer	prey

consumer	predator

Lesson Review 8

Circle the word that completes each sentence.

1. Living things get energy from _____ .

predators   **food**

2. A frog eats an insect. The frog

is a _____ .

predator   **prey**

3. A turtle eats a plant. The plant

is a _____ .

consumer   **producer**

4. All the food chains in a swamp make up

a _____ .

producer   **food web**

What is the water cycle?

Engage

Concept Poster 4 and Science Vocabulary Cards 33–38 *Whole group activity*

Build Background

Show children side A of card 33 (natural resource) and ask them to find a similar image on the poster. (water) Place card 33, image side out, in the pocket closest to the image. Say: *Natural resources are things that people can use. Water is a natural resource. What are some ways people use water?* (to drink, cook, clean) Read the sentence on side A of the card. Repeat with card 34 (water cycle), card 35 (evaporation), card 36 (condensation), card 37 (clouds), and card 38 (precipitation). Ask children the following questions:

- *What parts of the water cycle do you see?* (ocean, clouds, rain)
- *What kind of precipitation is falling from the clouds?* (rain)
- *When will water in the ocean enter the air as water vapor?* (during evaporation)
- *When will water vapor in the air form clouds?* (during condensation)

Explore and Learn

Inquiry Activity *Small group activity*

Model the Activity

- Place the materials for Activity Placemat 9 on each table, including copies of Activity Record Sheet 9 (p. 52).
- Model the correct pronunciation for each of the activity materials (paper plates, wax paper, water, dropper, lamp, and cardboard). Have children repeat the words. Explain that they will explore what affects how fast water evaporates.
- Read the steps of Activity Placemat 9 (Explore Evaporation) aloud with children.
- Guide children as they work in small groups to complete the activity and Activity Record Sheet 9. Demonstrate how to use the dropper.
- Have each child work with a partner to complete the **Now Try This** activity.

Discuss the Activity

Invite children to discuss the activity and compare observations. Ask:

- *What did you do that acts like the wind?* (fanning)
- *What thing did you use that gives off heat like the Sun?* (the lamp)
- *What can speed up evaporation?* (heat and wind)

Vocabulary Words

natural resource, water cycle, evaporation, condensation, cloud, precipitation

Science Objectives

Children will:

- identify water as a natural resource
- describe the relationships among evaporation, condensation, and precipitation in the water cycle
- identify forms of precipitation
- observe rates of evaporation
- explain how heat and wind affect evaporation
- predict how increasing the rate of wind affects evaporation

TESOL/LA Objectives

Children will:

- use contextual clues
- gather and organize materials to complete a task
- follow oral and written directions
- record observations

Materials

- Concept Poster 4
- Science Vocabulary Cards 33–38
- Activity Placemat 9
- Activity Record Sheet 9
- Science Journal
- Science Content Picture Dictionary
- Flip Book Lesson 9
- Concept Web 9
- Radius™ Science Vocabulary Cards 33–38
- Transparency 9
- Lesson Review 9

Vocabulary Word Wall
Place these words on the Word Wall:

natural resource, water cycle, evaporation, condensation, cloud, precipitation

Have children copy the words in their Science Journals. Next, have children draw a picture to illustrate each word. Post the children's illustrations below the appropriate words on the Word Wall.

Cognates
For Spanish-speaking children, it may be helpful to post this cognate chart to show similarities between words in Spanish and English. Keep in mind that children have varying literacy levels in Spanish, and some may not be familiar with these words.

Cognates	
English	**Spanish**
cycle	ciclo
vapor	vapor
liquid	líquido
gas	gas

Science Content Picture Dictionary
For children needing additional help with vocabulary words, refer them to the Science Content Picture Dictionary.

Explain Concepts and Vocabulary
Flip Book *Whole group activity*

Build Background
Review the Concept Poster 4 activity from the **Engage** section. Ask:
- *Why is water an important natural resource?*
- *How does water move in the water cycle?*
- *What makes up a cloud?*

Read Flip Book, Lesson 9
- Point to the title and read it aloud. Have children repeat the words. Then ask children to brainstorm answers to the title question. If a child uses the words **water cycle,** or any other vocabulary words on the poster, point to the words on the Flip Book page.
- Read the first sentence, pointing to each word as you read. Have children repeat the words. Point to the ocean in the photo. Ask: *What natural resource do you see?* (water) Follow the same procedure for the clouds and rain.
- Read the second sentence, pointing to each word as you read. Have children repeat the words. Use a finger to trace the direction of the arrows in the water cycle shown in the photo. Discuss how the cycle has no end. Encourage children to suggest words they may know with *cycle* in them. (tricycle, bicycle, motorcycle)
- Point to the steps in the water cycle, in turn. Begin with the step concerning *evaporation.* Read each boldfaced word, pointing to each word in it as you read. Have children repeat the words. Then ask children these questions where appropriate for the steps: *What happens during evaporation?* (Water changes to a gas called water vapor.) *What is water vapor?* (water in the air) *What happens during condensation?* (Water vapor changes to water drops.) *What do water drops form?* (clouds) *What are some kinds of precipitation?* (rain, snow, or hail)
- Again, use a finger to trace the direction of the arrows in the water cycle. Read the captions, in turn, that explain the steps in the water cycle. Point to each word in a step as you read it. Have children repeat the words in the step. Vary the step that you begin with to help children understand that there is no beginning or ending step in the water cycle.

Make Connections
- Point to the **Make Connections** box. Have children look at the pictures while you read the statements below them. Then, as a whole group, provide the missing word(s) in each statement (evaporation, condensation, natural resource). Then read the completed statements along with the children.

Elaborate

Concept Web *Paired activity*

Distribute copies of Concept Web 9 (p. 53). Have each child work with a partner to complete the concept web. For children needing additional help with the web, refer them to the Concept Poster 4, Science Vocabulary Cards 33–38, and the Flip Book. When children have finished, ask volunteers to share and talk about their completed webs.

Radius™ Science Vocabulary Cards
Small group activity

Have children use the Radius™ Audio Learning System and Radius™ Science Vocabulary Cards 33–38 to practice listening to, reading, writing, and speaking each word. Then have children do one or more of the following activities in their Science Journals:

- Have children make a list of the ways they use water. Suggest they illustrate the different ways.
- Have children draw a picture of an outdoor scene that includes water. Encourage them to show several other natural resources in the scene. Tell them to write the following caption for their picture: "Natural resources we use." Help children label each natural resource in their scene.
- Show children how to make a chart with three columns. Label the columns *Evaporation, Condensation,* and *Precipitation.* Children should write key phrases that refer to a particular step of the water cycle in the appropriate columns. For example, these phrases might fit in the column labeled *Evaporation:* water to water vapor, liquid to gas.

Evaluate

Transparency 9 *Whole group activity*

Assess Vocabulary Knowledge

Use side B (definition side) of the Science Vocabulary Cards 33–38 to review the lesson vocabulary words. Then distribute a copy of Transparency 9 to each child. Have children cut out the words at the bottom of the page and place them in the correct boxes. Model the task for them by using Transparency 9. Invite volunteers to use each vocabulary word in a sentence.

Lesson Review 9 *Individual activity*

Assess Concept Knowledge

Distribute copies of Lesson Review 9 (p. 54). Read the directions aloud and verify children's understanding. For children whose literacy skills are emerging, consider reading the sentences aloud. When finished, review the correct answers with children.

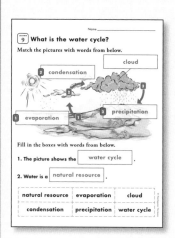

Explore Evaporation

4 | Observe and Record

Write the numbers 1, 2, and 3 to tell which drops dried first, next, and last.

Drop	How fast it dried
under lamp	
side of desk	
fanned	

5 | Share

Tell what can make water evaporate from Earth's land.

_____
_____
_____
_____
_____
_____
_____

Now Try This

Will fanning the water faster make it evaporate faster than fanning it slower? Try it and find out.

Prediction:_____

Results: _____

Concept Web 9

Draw a picture of each vocabulary word in the boxes below.

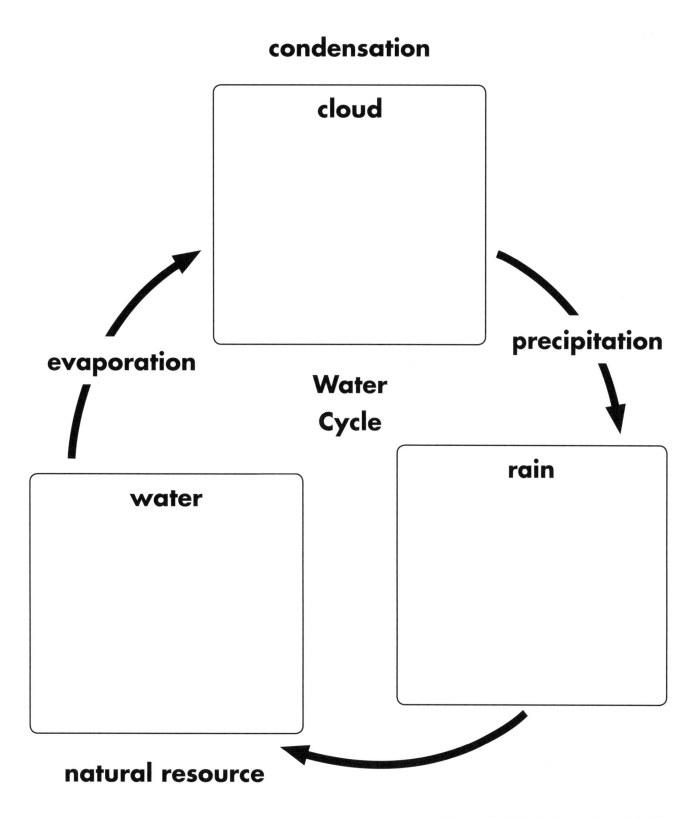

condensation

cloud

evaporation

precipitation

Water
Cycle

water

rain

natural resource

Lesson Review 9

**Write the word from the box that completes
each sentence.**

condensation	evaporation	natural resource
precipitation	clouds	water cycle

1. Water is a _____ .

2. Water vapor changes to water drops during

_____ .

3. Water changes to a gas during _____ .

4. Rain, snow, and hail are kinds of _____ .

5. Water moves in the _____ .

6. Water drops in the sky form _____ .

What are some kinds of weather?

Engage

Concept Poster 4 and Science Vocabulary
Card 39 *Whole group activity*

Build Background

Show children side A of card 39 (weather) and ask them to find a similar image on the poster. (rain) Place card 39, image side out, in the pocket closest to the image. Say: *The sunny day is changing. Soon it will rain.* Ask: *What will happen to the people if they stay outside?* (They will get wet.) Read the sentence on side A of the card.

Ask children the following questions:

* *What is the weather like when it is wet?*
* *What should you wear when the weather is wet?*
* *What is the weather like when it is sunny?*
* *What should you wear if it is sunny and hot outside?*
* *What are the people in the picture wearing? Is the weather hot or cold?*

Explore and Learn

Inquiry Activity *Small group activity*

Model the Activity

* Place the materials for Activity Placemat 10 on each table, including copies of Activity Record Sheet 10 (p. 58).
* Model the correct pronunciation for each of the activity materials (goggles, cups, tape, straw, pencil, paper clip, clay). Have children repeat the words. Explain that they are going to make a tool to measure wind.
* Read the steps of Activity Placemat 10 (Measure Wind) aloud with children.
* Guide children as they work in small groups to complete the activity and Activity Record Sheet 10. Caution children to handle the paper clip carefully. Show them how to use the paper clip so that they do not stick themselves.
* Have each child work with a partner to complete the **Now Try This** activity.

Discuss the Activity

Invite children to discuss the activity and compare observations. Ask:
* *How could you tell if the wind was blowing fast?*
* *How could you tell if the wind was blowing slow?*
* *How did the wind speed change from day to day?*
* *What was the weather like when the vane blew the fastest?*

Vocabulary Word
weather

Science Objectives
Children will:
* describe characteristics of hot, cold, wet, and windy weather
* identify weather changes
* make a model of a wind vane
* observe how a wind vane works
* measure wind speed

TESOL/LA Objectives
Children will:
* use contextual clues
* gather and organize materials to complete a task
* follow oral and written directions
* record observations

Materials
* Concept Poster 4
* Science Vocabulary Card 39
* Activity Placemat 10
* Activity Record Sheet 10
* Science Journal
* Science Content Picture Dictionary
* Flip Book Lesson 10
* Concept Web 10
* Radius™ Science Vocabulary Card 39
* Transparency 10
* Lesson Review 10

Vocabulary Word Wall

Place this word on the Word Wall:

weather

Have children copy the word in their Science Journals. Next, have children draw a picture to illustrate the word. Post the children's illustrations below the word on the Word Wall.

Cognates

For Spanish-speaking children, it may be helpful to post this cognate chart to show similarities between words in Spanish and English. Keep in mind that children have varying literacy levels in Spanish, and some may not be familiar with these words.

Cognates	
English	Spanish
air	aire

Science Content Picture Dictionary

For children needing additional help with vocabulary words, refer them to the Science Content Picture Dictionary.

Build Background

Review the Concept Poster 4 activity from the **Engage** section. Ask:

• *You see dark clouds and rain. What kind of weather is happening?*
• *You see few clouds in the sky. People are wearing T-shirts and shorts. What kind of weather is happening?*

Read Flip Book, Lesson 10

• Point to the title and read it aloud. Have children repeat the words. Then ask children to brainstorm answers to the title question. If a child uses the word **weather,** point to the word on the Flip Book page.
• Read the first sentence, pointing to each word as you read. Have children repeat the words. Point to the top left photo and say: *This picture shows hot weather.* Read the caption and have children repeat the word. Then ask: *How do you know that the weather is hot?* (Children are wearing T-shirts.) *Why do you think the children are pouring water on their heads?* (to cool down)
• Point to the top right photo and say: *This picture shows cold weather.* Read the caption and have children repeat the word. Then ask: *How can you tell that the weather is cold?* (Children are wearing snowsuits, boots, caps, scarves, and mittens. Snow is on the ground.)
• Point to the bottom left photo and say: *This picture shows wet weather.* Read the caption and have children repeat the word. Then ask: *How can you tell that the weather is wet?* (It is raining. Children are wearing raincoats and rain boots.)
• Point to the bottom right photo and say: *This picture shows windy weather.* Read the caption and have children repeat the word. Then ask: *How can you tell that the weather is windy?* (The girl is holding a blanket that is blowing in the wind.)
• Read the second sentence, pointing to each word as you read. Have children repeat the words. Talk about what your weather is like outside. Ask: *Is the weather today hot, cold, wet, or windy?*

Make Connections

• Point to the **Make Connections** box and read the statement aloud. Have children look at the pictures. Then, as a whole group, decide what the weather is like in each picture. Ask: *What is the weather like in the picture on the left?* (cloudy and rainy) *What is the weather like in the picture on the right?* (sunny with few clouds)

Elaborate

Concept Web *Paired activity*

Distribute copies of Concept Web 10 (p. 59). Have each child work with a partner to complete the concept web. For children needing additional help with the web, refer them to the Concept Poster 4, Science Vocabulary Card 39, and the Flip Book. When children have finished, ask volunteers to share and talk about their completed webs.

Radius™ Science Vocabulary Card
Small group activity

Have children use the Radius™ Audio Learning System and Radius™ Science Vocabulary Card 39 to practice listening to, reading, writing, and speaking the word. Then have children do one or more of the following activities in their Science Journals:

- Show children how to make a chart with five columns. Have them label the columns *Monday, Tuesday, Wednesday, Thursday,* and *Friday*. Tell children that they should show the weather for five days. They should draw one picture for each day. Then they should write a sentence that tells what the weather is like each day (hot, cold, wet, or windy).
- Help the children list words that describe the weather, such as hot, cold, wet, windy, rainy, snowy, cloudy, sunny, and foggy. Each day have them observe the weather and use the words on their list to describe it.
- Have children look in magazines and newspapers for pictures showing activities children can do during different kinds of weather. Tell them to cut out and sort the pictures into four groups: *hot weather activities, cold weather activities, wet weather activities,* and *windy weather activities*. Then have children paste the pictures, by group, into their Science Journal. Tell children to label each group.

Evaluate

Transparency 10 *Whole group activity*

Assess Vocabulary Knowledge

Use side B (definition side) of the Science Vocabulary Card 39 to review the lesson vocabulary word. Then distribute a copy of Transparency 10 to each child. Have children cut out the pictures at the bottom of the page and place them in the correct boxes. Model the task for them by using Transparency 10. Invite volunteers to use each vocabulary word in a sentence.

Lesson Review 10 *Individual activity*

Assess Concept Knowledge

Distribute copies of Lesson Review 10 (p. 60). Read the directions aloud and verify children's understanding. For children whose literacy skills are emerging, consider reading the sentences aloud. When finished, review the correct answers with children.

Home Connection

Send the completed copy of Activity Record Sheet 10 (p. 58) home with each child to share with his or her family.

Send a second copy of Transparency 10 home with each child for extra review and practice. Encourage children to work with family members to cut out and place pictures in the appropriate places on the transparency copy. Children can use the transparency copy to review vocabulary words throughout the school year.

Measure Wind

5 Record

- Tell how many times the wind vane turns in 1 minute each day.

Day	Time	Number of turns
1		
2		
3		
4		
5		

6 Share

- Tell which day had the fastest wind.

_____

Now Try This

Attach paper triangles to the straw. Which wind vane will catch the most wind? Why?

_____

_____

_____

Note to Parents: Use this sheet to review a science inquiry activity that your child did in class.

Concept Web 10

Fill in the blanks to write the vocabulary word. Draw a picture of the vocabulary word. Show the weather for today.

___ **eathe** ___

Lesson Review 10

Draw a picture to show the weather today where you live.

```
┌─────────────────────────────────────┐
│                                     │
│                                     │
│                                     │
│                                     │
│                                     │
│                                     │
│                                     │
│                                     │
└─────────────────────────────────────┘
```

Circle the word in each sentence that tells about the weather in the picture.

1. The weather is _____ .
    cold   **hot**

2. The weather is _____ .
    dry   **wet**

3. The weather is _____ .
    windy   **not windy**

How does Earth's land change?

Engage

Concept Poster 4 and Science Vocabulary
Cards 40–42 *Whole group activity*

Build Background

Show children side A of card 40 (weathering) and ask them to find a similar image on the poster. (cracks in rock, broken rocks) Place card 40, image side out, in the pocket closest to the image. Say: *Weathering caused this rock to break. Have you seen broken rocks? Where?* Read the sentence on side A of the card. Repeat with card 41 (erosion) and card 42 (pollution).

Ask children the following questions:
* *What does weathering do to rocks?*
* *Can water cause rocks to break? Can wind cause rocks to break? Can living things cause rocks to break?*
* *What does erosion move? How does erosion move things?*
* *Where can you see pollution?*
* *Is pollution good or bad?*

Explore and Learn

Inquiry Activity *Small group activity*

Model the Activity

* Place the materials for Activity Placemat 11 on each table, including copies of Activity Record Sheet 11 (p. 64).
* Model the correct pronunciation for each of the activity materials (colored chalk, jar with lid, water, strainer, hand lens, and paper). Have children repeat the words. Explain that the strainer is used to separate the pieces of chalk from water.
* Read the steps of Activity Placemat 11 (Model Erosion) aloud with children.
* Guide children as they work in small groups to complete the activity and Activity Record Sheet 11. Help children use the hand lens to look at the chalk pieces.
* Have each child work with a partner to complete the **Now Try This** activity.

Discuss the Activity

Invite children to discuss the activity and compare observations. Ask:
* *What did the chalk look like at first?*
* *How did it change in the water?*
* *What did the water do to the chalk?*

Vocabulary Words
weathering, erosion, pollution

Science Objectives
Children will:
* identify how Earth changes and what causes changes
* model erosion
* explain how weathering and erosion change rocks
* describe how pollution harms the land and living things

TESOL/LA Objectives
Children will:
* understand and produce technical vocabulary
* use contextual clues
* explain change
* record observations
* follow oral and written directions

Materials
* Concept Poster 4
* Science Vocabulary Cards 40–42
* Activity Placemat 11
* Activity Record Sheet 11
* Science Journal
* Science Content Picture Dictionary
* Flip Book Lesson 11
* Concept Web 11
* Radius™ Science Vocabulary Cards 40–42
* Transparency 11
* Lesson Review 11

Explain Concepts and Vocabulary

Flip Book *Whole group activity*

Build Background

Review the Concept Poster 11 activity from the **Engage** section. Ask:

* *How does weathering affect rocks?*
* *What moves rocks and soil?*
* *Where can you see pollution?*

Read Flip Book, Lesson 11

* Point to the title and read it aloud. Have children repeat the words. Then ask children to brainstorm answers to the title question. If a child uses the words **weathering, erosion,** or **pollution,** point to the words on the Flip Book page.
* Read the sentence, pointing to each word as you read. Have children repeat the words. Point to the photo of weathering and say: *This rock changed. What happened to this rock?* (It broke.) Read the caption and have children repeat the words. Then ask: *What caused this rock to break?* (weathering)
* Point to the photo of pollution and read the caption. Have children repeat the words. Ask: *Where is the pollution?* (on the beach) *What does pollution harm?* (living things) Explain to children that pollution harms living things because it destroys their environment.
* Point to the photo of erosion and read the caption. Have children repeat the words. Ask: *What changed this rock?* (erosion) Have students point to the parts of the rock that are missing due to erosion.

Make Connections

* Point to the **Make Connections** box and read the sentence aloud. Then, as a whole group, decide how Earth's land was changed in each picture. (arch: erosion carried away some of the rock; beach: pollution harms living things on the beach; cliff: weathering made holes in the rock) Ask: *What was changed by erosion and weathering?* (rocks) *What was changed by pollution?* (beach)

Vocabulary Word Wall

Place these words on the Word Wall:

weathering, erosion, pollution

Have children copy the words in their Science Journals. Next, have children draw a picture to illustrate each word. Photocopy and post the children's illustrations below the appropriate words on the Word Wall.

Cognates

For Spanish-speaking children, it may be helpful to post this cognate chart to show similarities between words in Spanish and English. Keep in mind that children have varying literacy levels in Spanish, and some may not be familiar with these words.

Cognates	
English	Spanish
erosion	erosión

Science Content Picture Dictionary

For children needing additional help with vocabulary words, refer them to the Science Content Picture Dictionary.

Elaborate

Concept Web *Paired activity*

Distribute copies of Concept Web 11 (p. 65). Have each child work with a partner to complete the concept web. For children needing additional help with the web, refer them to Concept Poster 4, Science Vocabulary Cards 40–42, and the Flip Book. When children have finished, ask volunteers to share and talk about their completed webs.

Radius™ Science Vocabulary Cards
Small group activity

Have children use the Radius™ Audio Learning System and Radius™ Science Vocabulary Cards 40–42 to practice listening to, reading, writing, and speaking each word. Then have children do one or more of the following activities in their Science Journals:

- Have children find examples of weathering and erosion in magazine photos. Have them cut out the pictures and paste them in their Science Journals. Tell students to write a caption for each picture.
- Have children find examples of pollution in magazines. Have them cut out the pictures and paste them in their Science Journals. Have them write a caption that describes each picture. Then have them draw a picture of what the area would look like if there was no pollution.
- Invite children to use their own words to write definitions of the vocabulary words. Have them illustrate their definitions.

Evaluate

Transparency 11 *Whole group activity*

Assess Vocabulary Knowledge

Use side B (definition side) of the Science Vocabulary Cards 40–42 to review the lesson vocabulary words. Then distribute a copy of Transparency 11 to each child. Have children cut out the pictures at the bottom of the page and place them in the correct boxes. Model the task for them by using Transparency 11. Invite volunteers to use each vocabulary word in a sentence.

Lesson Review 11 *Individual activity*

Assess Concept Knowledge

Distribute copies of Lesson Review 11 (p. 66). Read the directions aloud and verify children's understanding. For children whose literacy skills are emerging, consider reading the sentences aloud. When finished, review the correct answers with children.

Home Connection

Send the completed copy of Activity Record Sheet 11 (p. 64) home with each child to share with his or her family.

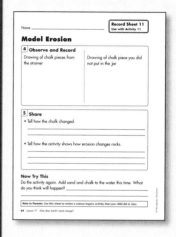

Send a second copy of Transparency 11 home with each child for extra review and practice. Encourage children to work with family members to cut out and place vocabulary words in the appropriate places on the transparency copy. Children can use the transparency copy to review vocabulary words throughout the school year.

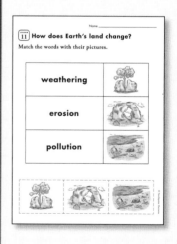

Model Erosion

4 Observe and Record

Drawing of chalk pieces from the strainer	Drawing of chalk piece you did not put in the jar

5 Share

• Tell how the chalk changed.

_____

_____

• Tell how the activity shows how erosion changes rocks.

_____

_____

_____

Now Try This

Do the activity again. Add sand and chalk to the water this time. What do you think will happen? _____

_____

Note to Parents: Use this sheet to review a science inquiry activity that your child did in class.

© Northpoint Horizons™

Concept Web 11

Fill in the blanks to write the vocabulary words. Draw a picture of each vocabulary word.

1. ___eatherin___ is when living things, water, or wind breaks rocks.

2. ___rosio___ is when wind or water moves soil or rock.

3. ___ollutio___ harms living things.

Lesson Review 11

Read each sentence about how Earth's land changes.

Circle the word to tell if the change is erosion, pollution, or weathering.

1. The roots of a tree cause a rock to break apart.

erosion　　　**pollution**　　　**weathering**

2. Water moves pieces of rock.

erosion　　　**pollution**　　　**weathering**

3. A lot of trash covers a beach.

erosion　　　**pollution**　　　**weathering**

What are seasons?

Engage
Concept Poster 4 and Science Vocabulary
Cards 43–45 *Whole group activity*

Build Background
Show children side A of card 43 (season) and ask them to find a similar image on the poster (the trees). Place card 43, image side out, in the pocket closest to the image. Say: *These trees change in different seasons. Which tree on the card looks most like these trees on the poster?* (the colorful autumn tree) Read the sentence on side A of the card. Repeat with card 44 (temperature) and card 45 (thermometer).
Ask children the following questions:
* *What do you think the temperature is like in this poster? Why?*
* *How do you measure temperature?*
* *What would the season be if the trees on the poster looked like this?* (point to winter trees on vocabulary card)

Explore and Learn
Inquiry Activity *Small group activity*

Model the Activity
* Place the materials for Activity Placemat 12 on each table, including copies of Activity Record Sheet 12 (p. 70).
* Model the correct pronunciation for each of the activity materials (cups, warm water, cold water, thermometers, craft stick thermometers, paper, tape, and red crayon). Have children repeat the words.
* Read the steps of Activity Placemat 12 (Explore Thermometers and Temperature) aloud with children.
* Guide children as they work in small groups to complete the activity and Activity Record Sheet 12. Help children keep track of time, and read the thermometers to color and label their craft stick thermometers.
* Have each child work with a partner to complete the **Now Try This** activity.

Discuss the Activity
Invite children to discuss the activity and compare observations. Ask:
* *Which thermometer had a higher line, cold or warm?*
* *What do you think a thermometer would show if we put it in a cup of ice cream?*
* *What would a thermometer show if we put it in a cup of hot tea?*

Vocabulary Words
season, temperature, thermometer

Science Objectives
Children will:
* identify the four seasons
* observe how thermometers measure temperature
* interpret and record observations

TESOL/LA Objectives
Children will:
* understand and produce technical vocabulary
* follow oral and written directions
* participate in full class, group, and pair discussions
* compare and contrast information
* represent information visually and interpret information presented visually
* identify and associate written symbols with words

Materials
* Concept Poster 4
* Science Vocabulary Cards 43–45
* Activity Placemat 12
* Activity Record Sheet 12
* Science Journal
* Science Content Picture Dictionary
* Flip Book Lesson 12
* Concept Web 12
* Radius™ Science Vocabulary Cards 43–45
* Transparency 12
* Lesson Review 12

Explain Concepts and Vocabulary

Flip Book *Whole group activity*

Build Background

Review the Concept Poster 4 activity from the **Engage** section. Ask:

- *What changes with each season?*
- *Are the people in this poster going to measure temperature? How do you know?*

Read Flip Book, Lesson 12

- Point to the title and read it aloud. Have children repeat the words. Then ask children to brainstorm answers to the title question. If a child uses the words **weather** or **temperature,** point to the words on the Flip Book page.
- Read the first sentence, pointing to each word as you read. Have children repeat the words. Point to the spring photo and say: *In this picture it is spring.* Ask: *What happens to trees in spring?* (Trees get leaves.)
- Point to the summer photo. Read the caption and have children repeat the word. Ask: *What happens to trees in summer?* (Trees are very green.)
- Point to the autumn photo. Read and have children repeat the word. Ask: *What happens to trees in autumn?* (Leaves turn colors.)
- Point to the winter photo. Read and have children repeat the word. Ask: *What happens to trees in winter?* (Trees have no leaves.)
- Read the second sentence, pointing to each word as you read. Have children repeat the words. Then read the third sentence, pointing to each word as you read. Have children repeat the words. Ask: *What do we use to measure temperature?* (a thermometer) *How does the temperature change from spring to summer?* (temperature gets higher) *How does the temperature change from summer to autumn?* (temperature gets lower) *How does the temperature change from autumn to winter?* (temperature gets even lower) *What season is the coldest?* (winter) *How do you know?* (The thermometer has the shortest line so the temperature is lowest.)

Make Connections

- Point to the **Make Connections** box and read the statement aloud. Then, as a whole group, tell what the children are doing in each photo. (picking flowers, playing in leaves, swimming) Ask: *When do leaves and flowers start to grow?* (spring) *When do leaves fall off trees so children can play in the leaves?* (autumn) *What season is good for swimming?* (summer) *Why?* (It is hot.)

Vocabulary Word Wall
Place these words on the Word Wall:

season, temperature, thermometer

Have children copy the words in their Science Journals. Next, have children draw a picture to illustrate each word. Photocopy and post the children's illustrations below the appropriate words on the Word Wall.

Cognates
For Spanish-speaking children, it may be helpful to post this cognate chart to show similarities between words in Spanish and English. Keep in mind that children have varying literacy levels in Spanish, and some may not be familiar with these words.

Cognates	
English	**Spanish**
season	estación
temperature	temperatura
thermometer	termómetro

Science Content Picture Dictionary
For children needing additional help with vocabulary words, refer them to the Science Content Picture Dictionary.

Elaborate

Concept Web *Paired activity*

Distribute copies of Concept Web 12 (p. 71). Have each child work with a partner to draw and color pictures showing each season. For additional help with the web, refer them to the Concept Poster 4, Science Vocabulary Cards 43–45, and the Flip Book. When children have finished, ask volunteers to share and talk about their completed webs. Ask children to tell what they think the temperature is in each picture.

Radius™ Science Vocabulary Cards
Small group activity

Have children use the Radius™ Audio Learning System and Radius™ Science Vocabulary Cards 43–45 to practice listening to, reading, writing, and speaking each word. Then have children do one or more of the following activities in their Science Journals:

- Provide children with magazines that include photos of the four seasons. Have them cut out and sort the pictures into four groups: *spring, summer, autumn,* and *winter.* (If no magazines are available have children draw pictures of what they like to do in each season.) Then have children paste their drawings or groups of photos into their Science Journals. Guide children to label and draw a thermometer by each picture or group. Encourage children to write captions for their pictures.
- Have children draw thermometers that show the temperatures in various settings, such as outside in winter or in a bowl of hot soup. Help children label their drawings *hot, cold, warm,* or *cool,* and paste them into their Science Journals.
- Invite children to use their own words to write a definition of each vocabulary word. Have them illustrate their definitions.

Evaluate

Transparency 12 *Whole group activity*

Assess Vocabulary Knowledge

Use side B (definition side) of the Science Vocabulary Cards 43–45 to review the lesson vocabulary words. Then distribute a copy of Transparency 12 to each child. Have children cut out the vocabulary words at the bottom of the page and place each in the correct boxes. Model the task for them by using Transparency 12. Invite volunteers to use each vocabulary word in a sentence.

Lesson Review 12 *Individual activity*

Assess Concept Knowledge

Distribute copies of Lesson Review 12 (p. 72). Read the directions aloud and verify children's understanding. For children whose literacy skills are emerging, consider reading the sentences aloud. When finished, review the correct answers with children.

Home Connection

Send the completed copy of Activity Record Sheet 12 (p. 70) home with each child to share with his or her family.

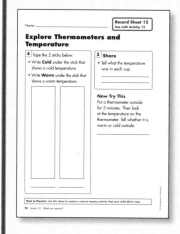

Send a second copy of Transparency 12 home with each child for extra review and practice. Encourage children to work with family members to cut out and place vocabulary words in the appropriate places on the transparency copy. Children can use the transparency copy to review vocabulary words throughout the school year.

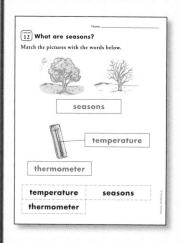

Explore Thermometers and Temperature

4 Tape the 2 sticks below.

- Write **Cold** under the stick that shows a cold temperature.
- Write **Warm** under the stick that shows a warm temperature.

_____ _____

5 **Share**

- Tell what the temperature was in each cup.

_____

_____

Now Try This

Put a thermometer outside for 5 minutes. Then look at the temperature on the thermometer. Tell whether it is warm or cold outside.

_____

Note to Parents: Use this sheet to review a science inquiry activity that your child did in class.

Concept Web 12

Draw a picture of each season.

Spring	**Summer**

Autumn	**Winter**

Lesson Review 12

Write the word from the box that completes each sentence.

season	temperature	thermometer

1. The _____ is how hot or cold it is outside.

2. Weather changes with each new _____ .

3. You measure temperature with a _____ .

Draw a picture of one season where you live. Write the name of the season below your picture.

Engage

Concept Poster 4 and Science Vocabulary Cards 46–48 *Whole group activity*

Build Background

Show children side A of card 46 (investigate) and ask them to find a similar image on the poster (the scientists on the cliff). Place card 46, image side out, in the pocket closest to the image. Say: *These scientists are investigating. How are they different from the ones on the card?* (They are outside; not wearing lab coats.) Read the sentence on side A of the card. Repeat with card 47 (dinosaur) and card 48 (fossil).

Ask children the following questions:

- *What do scientists do when they investigate?*
- *What are the scientists in the poster investigating?*
- *Where do scientists find dinosaur fossils?*
- *How do you know?*

Explore and Learn

Inquiry Activity *Small group activity*

Model the Activity

- Place the materials for Activity Placemat 13 on each table, including copies of Activity Record Sheet 13 (p. 76).
- Model the correct pronunciation for each of the activity materials (paper, crayons, scissors, glue). Have children repeat the words. Explain that they are going to infer from evidence like scientists do.
- Read the steps of Activity Placemat 13 (Infer From Picture Clues) aloud with children.
- Guide children as they work in small groups to complete the activity and Activity Record Sheet 13. Help children cut and glue their pictures, and determine how to complete the missing pieces.
- Have each child work with a partner to complete the **Now Try This** activity.

Discuss the Activity

Invite children to discuss the activity and compare observations. Ask:

- *Was it hard to put together your partner's pieces? Would it be easier if all the pieces were there? Why?*
- *Do you think pieces are missing when scientists find real dinosaur fossils?*
- *How did you decide what to draw for the missing pieces?*

Vocabulary Words
investigate, dinosaur, fossil

Science Objectives
Children will:

- describe why scientists investigate
- infer what a dinosaur looks like from partial evidence
- tell what a fossil is
- discuss how scientists learn about dinosaurs

TESOL/LA Objectives
Children will:

- understand and produce technical vocabulary
- participate in full class, group, and pair discussions
- analyze, synthesize, and infer from information
- represent information visually and interpret information presented visually
- use contextual clues

Materials

- Concept Poster 4
- Science Vocabulary Cards 46–48
- Activity Placemat 13
- Activity Record Sheet 13
- Science Journal
- Science Content Picture Dictionary
- Flip Book Lesson 13
- Concept Web 13
- Radius™ Science Vocabulary Cards 46–48
- Transparency 13
- Lesson Review 13

Vocabulary Word Wall

Place these words on the Word Wall:

investigate, dinosaur, fossil

Have children copy the words in their Science Journals. Next, have children draw a picture to illustrate each word. Photocopy and post the children's illustrations below the appropriate words on the Word Wall.

Cognates

For Spanish-speaking children, it may be helpful to post this cognate chart to show similarities between words in Spanish and English. Keep in mind that children have varying literacy levels in Spanish, and some may not be familiar with these words.

Cognates	
English	**Spanish**
investigate	investigar
dinosaur	dinosaurio
fossil	fósil

Science Content Picture Dictionary

For children needing additional help with vocabulary words, refer them to the Science Content Picture Dictionary.

Explain Concepts and Vocabulary

Flip Book *Whole group activity*

Build Background

Review the Concept Poster 4 activity from the **Engage** section. Ask:

- *What do scientists investigate?*
- *Why are these scientists studying a dinosaur?*
- *What is a fossil?*

Read Flip Book, Lesson 6

- Point to the title and read it aloud. Have children repeat the words. Then ask children to brainstorm answers to the title question. If a child uses the words **investigate, dinosaur,** or **fossil,** point to the words on the Flip Book page.
- Read the sentence, pointing to each word as you read. Have children repeat the words. Point to the photo of the scientists and say: *These scientists are investigating in a laboratory. What kinds of things are in a science laboratory?* (test tubes, droppers) *What are these scientists wearing?* (white lab coats, gloves) *Why might they want to wear these things?* (to keep chemicals away from their clothes or skin)
- Point to the photo of the dinosaur skeleton and read the caption. Have children repeat the words. Ask: *What parts of the dinosaur are here?* (the bones) Tell the children that *skeleton* is a word for the bones in an animal's body.
- Point to the three photos of the fossils and read the sentence caption. Have children repeat the sentence. Then read the caption under each photo. Have children repeat the words. Ask: *Do these pictures show any bones?* (no) *How can fossils help scientists learn more about dinosaurs?* (They can show the eggs, teeth, and footprints of dinosaurs.)

Make Connections

- Point to the **Make Connections** box and read the sentences. Then, as a group, name the things shown. (leaves, fish, shell, seastar, dragonfly) Ask: *Are all of these fossils of animals?* (no) *Which picture shows part of a plant?* (leaves)

Elaborate

Concept Web *Paired activity*

Distribute copies of Concept Web 13 (p. 77). Have each child work with a partner to complete the concept web. For children needing additional help with the web, refer them to the Concept Poster 4, Science Vocabulary Cards 46–48, and the Flip Book. When children have finished, ask volunteers to share and talk about their completed webs.

Radius™ Science Vocabulary Cards

Small group activity

Have children use the Radius™ Audio Learning System and Radius™ Science Vocabulary Cards 46–48 to practice listening to, reading, writing, and speaking each word. Then have children do one or more of the following activities in their Science Journals:

- Have children draw pictures of scientists investigating in various settings, such as in a lab or outdoors. Have them paste the drawings into their Science Journals. Encourage children to write captions for their pictures.
- Provide children with clay, and have them make models of dinosaur bones and skeletons or press objects, such as leaves or their thumbs, into disks of clay to make models of fossils. Help children write captions for their finished products, and display them in the room.
- Invite children to use their own words to write a definition of each vocabulary word. Have them illustrate their definitions.

Evaluate

Transparency 13 *Whole group activity*

Assess Vocabulary Knowledge

Use side B (definition side) of the Science Vocabulary Cards 46–48 to review the lesson vocabulary words. Then distribute a copy of Transparency 13 to each child. Have children cut out the pictures at the bottom of the page and place them in the correct boxes. Model the task for them by using Transparency 13. Invite volunteers to use each vocabulary word in a sentence.

Lesson Review 13 *Individual activity*

Assess Concept Knowledge

Distribute copies of Lesson Review 13 (p. 78). Read the directions aloud and verify children's understanding. For children whose literacy skills are emerging, consider reading the sentences aloud. When finished, review the correct answers with children.

Home Connection

Send the completed copy of Activity Record Sheet 13 (p. 76) home with each child to share with his or her family.

Send a second copy of Transparency 13 home with each child for extra review and practice. Encourage children to work with family members to cut out and place vocabulary words in the appropriate places on the transparency copy. Children can use the transparency copy to review vocabulary words throughout the school year.

Infer From Picture Clues

5 Draw your partner's dinosaur. Draw the missing pieces in the right place.

6 **Share**

Compare what you drew with the missing pieces.

_____
_____
_____
_____

Now Try This

Do the activity again. Cut your drawing into smaller pieces.
Compare what you drew with the missing pieces.

_____
_____
_____
_____

Note to Parents: Use this sheet to review a science inquiry activity that your child did in class.

Concept Web 13

Fill in the blanks to write the vocabulary words. Draw a picture of each vocabulary word.

____ossil

____inosau____

____nvestigate

Lesson Review 13

Circle the answer to each question.

1. What is a dinosaur?

an animal that lives with scientists
an animal that lived on Earth long ago

2. What is a fossil?

a print of an animal or living thing that lived
long ago
the name of a dinosaur

Draw a picture to show what scientists investigate.

© Northpoint Horizons™

What is matter?

Engage

Concept Poster 5 and Science Vocabulary Cards 49–50 *Whole group activity*

Build Background

Show children side A of card 49 (matter) and ask them to find a similar image on the poster (the picnic table). Place card 49, image side out, in the pocket closest to the image. Say: *The table is made of matter.* Read the sentence on side A of the card. Ask: *What are some other objects in the poster that are matter?* (trees, cup, balloons, etc.) Repeat with card 50 (mass).

Ask children the following questions:

* *Are the people made of matter? Is the dog made of matter?*
* *Which person do you think has the most mass?*
* *Which has more mass—the toy balloons or the hot-air balloon?*
* *Which has more mass—the pitcher of lemonade or a cup of lemonade? What tool could you use to find out?* (a balance)

Explore and Learn

Inquiry Activity *Small group activity*

Model the Activity

* Place the materials for Activity Placemat 14 on each table, including copies of Activity Record Sheet 14 (p. 82).
* Model the correct pronunciation for each of the activity materials (cups, tape, ruler, pencil). Have children repeat the words. Explain that they are going to make a balance to compare mass.
* Read the steps of Activity Placemat 14 (Measure Mass) aloud with children.
* Guide children as they work in small groups to complete the activity and Activity Record Sheet 14. Help children understand what it means to predict, or guess, which object has more mass.
* Have each child work with a partner to complete the **Now Try This** activity.

Discuss the Activity

Invite children to discuss the activity and compare observations. Ask:

* *What two small objects did your group put on the balance?*
* *Which of the objects has more mass? How did you know?*
* *Was your prediction in Step 3 correct? Why or why not?*
* *Which had more mass in the **Now Try This**—the sand or the stones?*

Vocabulary Words

matter, mass

Science Objectives

Children will:

* tell what matter is and give examples
* construct a balance
* predict which object has more mass
* compare the masses of objects
* determine that all matter takes up space

TESOL/LA Objectives

Children will:

* understand and produce technical vocabulary
* use contextual clues
* compare objects
* follow oral and written directions
* make predictions
* record observations

Materials

* Concept Poster 5
* Science Vocabulary Cards 49–50
* Activity Placemat 14
* Activity Record Sheet 14
* Science Journal
* Science Content Picture Dictionary
* Flip Book Lesson 14
* Concept Web 14
* Radius™ Science Vocabulary Cards 49–50
* Transparency 14
* Lesson Review 14

Explain Concepts and Vocabulary

Flip Book *Whole group activity*

Build Background

Review the Concept Poster 5 activity from the **Engage** section. Ask:
- *Which thing in the poster do you think has the most mass?*
- *Does a child or an adult have more mass?*
- *Is there anything you see in the poster that is not made of matter?* (no)

Read Flip Book, Lesson 14

- Point to the title and read it aloud. Have children repeat the words. Then ask children to brainstorm answers to the title question. If a child uses the word **matter** or the names of any of the pictured objects, point to the words on the Flip Book page.
- Read the first sentence, pointing to each word as you read. Have children repeat the words. Point to the photo and say: *All the things you can see in the picture take up space, so they are all matter.* Ask: *Are the boys matter? What other things in the picture are matter?*
- Read the second sentence, pointing to each word as you read. Have children repeat the words. Point to the photo and say: *All the things you see in the picture have mass.* Ask: *Do the boys have mass? What other things in the picture have mass?* Read the caption and have children repeat the words. Then ask: *What can you use to compare the masses of objects?*

Make Connections

- Point to the **Make Connections** box and read the questions aloud. Then, as a whole group, decide which objects have mass. (all of them) Then decide which objects take up space. (all of them) Ask: *Which pictures show objects that are made of matter?* (all of them)

Elaborate

Concept Web *Paired activity*

Distribute copies of Concept Web 14 (p. 83). Have each child work with a partner to complete the concept web. For children needing additional help with the web, refer them to the Concept Poster 5, Science Vocabulary Cards 49–50, and the Flip Book. When children have finished, ask volunteers to share and talk about their completed webs.

Radius™ Science Vocabulary Cards

Small group activity

Have children use the Radius™ Audio Learning System and Radius™ Science Vocabulary Cards 49–50 to practice listening to, reading, writing, and speaking each word. Then have children do one or more of these writing activities in their Science Journals:

- Have children think about their favorite foods. Have them draw pictures of those foods. Have them write a sentence telling whether their favorite foods are matter and how they know.
- Have children draw a picture of a blown-up balloon. Have them work with a partner to decide if the air in the balloon takes up space. Then ask them to write one or two sentences telling whether air is made of matter and how they know.
- Invite children to make a matter alphabet, writing one word for each letter. Have children work with a partner to brainstorm names of objects made of matter that they can use.

Evaluate

Transparency 14 *Whole group activity*

Assess Vocabulary Knowledge

Use side B (definition side) of the Science Vocabulary Cards 49–50 to review the lesson vocabulary words. Then distribute a copy of Transparency 14 to each child. Have children cut out the vocabulary words at the bottom of the page and place them in the correct boxes. Model the task for them by using Transparency 14. Invite volunteers to use each vocabulary word in a sentence.

Lesson Review 14 *Individual activity*

Assess Concept Knowledge

Distribute copies of Lesson Review 14 (p. 84). Read the directions aloud and verify children's understanding. For children whose literacy skills are emerging, consider reading the sentences aloud. When finished, review the correct answers with children.

Home Connection

Send the completed copy of Activity Record Sheet 14 (p. 82) home with each child to share with his or her family.

Send a second copy of Transparency 14 home with each child for extra review and practice. Encourage children to work with family members to cut out and place vocabulary words in the appropriate places on the transparency copy. Children can use the transparency copy to review vocabulary words throughout the school year.

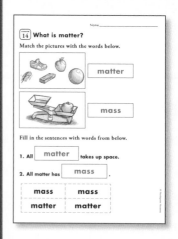

Measure Mass

3

Predict which object you think has more mass.

- Write your prediction.

_____
_____
_____

4 **Explore and Observe**

Observe the cups.

- Which cup is higher?

_____

- Which cup has more mass?

_____

5 **Share**

- Tell whether your prediction was correct.

_____

- Tell how you know.

_____
_____
_____

Now Try This

Which do you think has more mass—a half cup of sand or a half cup of stones? Use your balance to find out.

Prediction: _____

Results: _____

Note to Parents: Use this sheet to review a science inquiry activity that your child did in class.

Concept Web 14

Fill in the blanks to write the vocabulary words. Then draw a picture to show each vocabulary word.

___ atte ___ takes up space and has mass.

You can use a balance to find the
___ as ___ of an object.

Lesson Review 14

Write the word from the box that completes each sentence.

balance	mass	matter

1. All _____ takes up space.

2. All matter has _____ .

3. You can measure mass with a _____ .

Draw a picture of something that is matter.

What forms does matter take?

Engage

Concept Poster 5 and Science Vocabulary Cards 51–54 *Whole group activity*

Build Background

Show children side A of card 51 (gas) and ask them to find a similar image on the poster. (balloon) Place card 51, image side out, in the pocket closest to the image. Say: *The fish breathes air. What is air?* (gases) *Where is the air in the tank?* (at the top, and in the water) *The balloon contains gases. Why do you think it floats?* (The gases inside the balloon are lighter than air.) Read the sentence on side A of the card. Repeat with card 52 (liquid), card 53 (solid), and card 54 (mixture).

Ask children the following questions:

* *What different forms does matter take?* (solids, liquids, gases, mixtures)
* *Which of the things in the picture are a gas?*
* *Which of the things in the picture are a liquid?*
* *Which of the things in the picture are a solid?*
* *Can you find things in the picture that are a mixture?*

Explore and Learn

Inquiry Activity *Small group activity*

Model the Activity

* Place the materials for Activity Placemat 15 on each table, including copies of Activity Record Sheet 15 (p. 88).
* Model the correct pronunciations for each of the activity materials (clay, balance, gram masses). Have children repeat the words. Explain that they will form the clay into a shape and measure its mass using the balance.
* Read the steps of Activity Placemat 15 (Explore Shape and Mass) aloud with children.
* Guide children as they work in small groups to complete the activity and Activity Record Sheet 15. Help children use the balance and recognize the size of the gram masses to accurately measure the mass of the clay.
* Have each child work with a partner to complete the **Now Try This** activity.

Discuss the Activity

Invite children to discuss the activity and compare observations. Ask:

* *Was it easy or difficult to change the shape of the clay?*
* *Did the mass of the clay change when you changed its shape?*
* *How did dividing the clay into smaller pieces affect its mass?*

Vocabulary Words

gas, liquid, solid, mixture

Science Objectives

Children will:

* describe the properties of different forms of matter
* classify matter as solids, liquids, gases, or mixtures
* understand how matter is measured
* tell how the shape of matter affects mass
* interpret visual information
* gather and organize materials to complete an activity
* record observations in chart form and interpret those observations

TESOL/LA Objectives

Children will:

* understand and produce technical vocabulary
* use contextual clues
* classify objects
* explain changes
* follow oral and written directions
* record observations

Materials

* Concept Poster 5
* Science Vocabulary Cards 51–54
* Activity Placemat 15
* Activity Record Sheet 15
* Science Journal
* Science Content Picture Dictionary
* Flip Book Lesson 15
* Concept Web 15
* Radius™ Science Vocabulary Cards 51–54
* Transparency 15
* Lesson Review 15

Place these words on the Word Wall:

gas, liquid, solid, mixture

Have children copy the words in their Science Journals. Next, have children draw a picture to illustrate each word. Photocopy and post the children's illustrations below the appropriate words on the Word Wall.

Cognates

For Spanish-speaking children, it may be helpful to post this cognate chart to show similarities between words in Spanish and English. Keep in mind that children have varying literacy levels in Spanish, and some may not be familiar with these words.

Cognates	
English	**Spanish**
gas	gas
liquid	líquido
solid	sólido
mass	masa

Science Content Picture Dictionary

For children needing additional help with vocabulary words, refer them to the Science Content Picture Dictionary.

Explain Concepts and Vocabulary
Flip Book *Whole group activity*

Build Background
Review the Concept Poster 5 activity from the **Engage** section. Ask:
- *What matter in the picture is a gas?*
- *What matter in the picture is a liquid?*
- *Name at least three things at the picnic that are solids.*
- *Which of the foods at the table are mixtures?*

Read Flip Book, Lesson 15
- Point to the title and read it aloud. Have children repeat the words. Then ask children to brainstorm answers to the title question. If a child uses any of the words **gas, liquid, solid, mixture,** point to the words on the Flip Book page.
- Read the sentence, pointing to each word as you read. Have children repeat the words. Point to the air at the top of the tank and the bubbles in the water near the air pump. Say: *This is air.* Read the caption and have children repeat the words. Then ask: *What gas does the fish need to breathe?* (air) *How does the fish breathe air?* (through its gills)
- Point to the water in the tank, and read the caption. Have children repeat the words. Ask: *Where do the fish live?* (in water)
- Point to the rock, and say: *This is the rock.* Read the caption and have children repeat the words. Ask: *Why do you think there are rocks and gravel in the tank?* (They give the water plants something to hold on to.) *What form of matter is the rock?* (solid) Point to the gravel and read the caption. Have children repeat the words. Ask: *What is the gravel made of?* (a mixture of different stones)

Make Connections
- Point to the **Make Connections** box and read the direction aloud. Then, as a whole group, name the matter shown in the pictures (water, air, stones). Ask: *What form of matter is water?* (The water is a liquid.) *What form of matter is air?* (The air is a gas.) *What form of matter is the stone?* (The stone is a solid.)

Elaborate

Concept Web *Paired activity*

Distribute copies of Concept Web 15 (p. 89). Have each child work with a partner to complete the concept web. For children needing additional help with the web, refer them to the Concept Poster 5, Science Vocabulary Cards 51–54, and the Flip Book. When children have finished, ask volunteers to share and talk about their completed webs.

Radius™ Science Vocabulary Cards
Small group activity

Have children use the Radius™ Audio Learning System and Radius™ Science Cards 51–54 to practice listening to, reading, writing, and speaking each word. Then have children do one or more of the following activities in their Science Journals:

- Have pairs of children draw a picture that shows at least three different forms of matter. Have them label the forms of matter at appropriate spots in their drawings.
- Distribute catalogs or science magazines to small groups of children. Have them look through the reference sources for pictures of examples of the different forms of matter. Have them cut out the pictures, sort them into groups, and paste them into their Science Journals. Encourage children to write captions telling what form of matter each group represents.
- Have children work in small groups to write sentences that incorporate each vocabulary word (solid, liquid, gas, mixture). Have them combine the sentences into a short paragraph that describes different forms of matter.

Evaluate

Transparency 15 *Whole group activity*

Assess Vocabulary Knowledge

Use side B (definition side) of the Science Vocabulary Cards 51–54 to review the lesson vocabulary words. Then distribute a copy of Transparency 15 to each child. Have children cut out the words at the bottom of the transparency and place them around the fish tank in the place closest to the correct form of matter. Model the task for them by using Transparency 15. Invite volunteers to use each vocabulary word in a sentence.

Lesson Review 15 *Individual activity*

Assess Concept Knowledge

Distribute copies of Lesson Review 15 (p. 90). Read the directions aloud and verify children's understanding. For children whose literacy skills are emerging, consider reading the sentences aloud. When finished, review the correct answers with children.

Home Connection

Send the completed copy of Activity Record Sheet 15 (p. 88) home with each child to share with his or her family.

Send a second copy of Transparency 15 home with each child for extra review and practice. Encourage children to work with family members to cut out and place vocabulary words in the appropriate places on the transparency copy. Children can use the transparency copy to review vocabulary words throughout the school year.

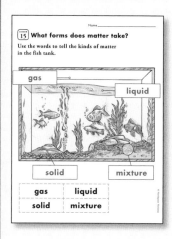

Explore Shape and Mass

4 Record

Draw the shapes you made in the chart.
Show the mass of the clay for each shape.

Shape of clay	Mass

5 Share

• Tell how changing the shape of matter affects mass.

_____

_____

Now Try This

Find the mass of some clay. Cut the clay into pieces.
Find the mass of all the pieces.

Mass of clay: _____

Mass of pieces: _____

Does the mass change? _____

Note to Parents: Use this sheet to review a science inquiry activity that your child did in class.

Concept Web 15

Draw a picture for each form of matter in the correct circle.

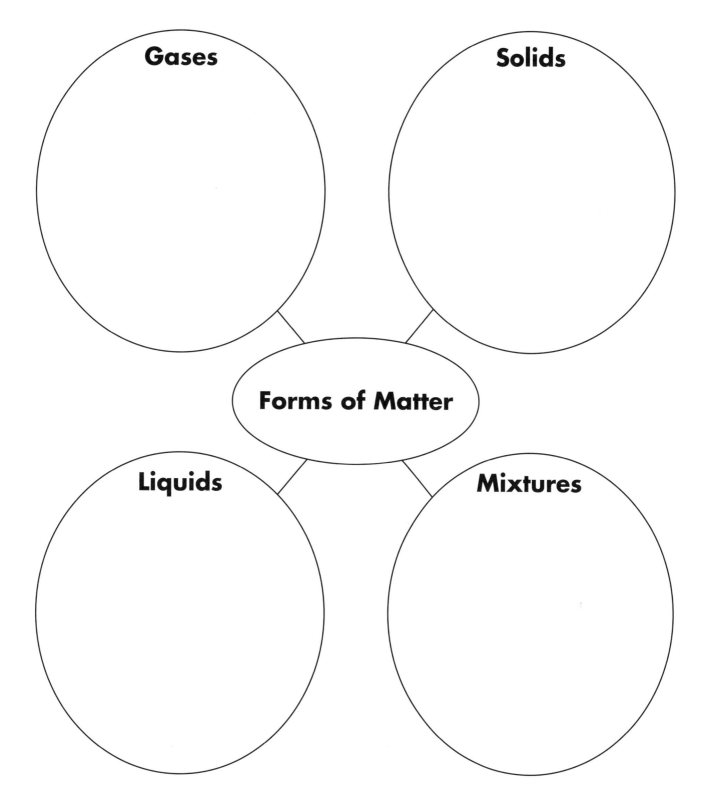

Gases

Solids

Forms of Matter

Liquids

Mixtures

Lesson Review 15

Circle the answer for each question.

1. Which is a solid?
rock   **water**

2. Which is a liquid?
air   **water**

3. Which is a gas?
air   **fish**

4. Which is a mixture?
gravel   **water**

Engage

Concept Poster 6 and Science Vocabulary Cards 55–58 *Whole group activity*

Build Background

Show children side A of card 55 (force) and ask them to find a similar image on the poster. (boy pushing toy train) Place card 55, image side out, in the pocket closest to the image. Say: *The boy is playing with a toy train.* Ask: *What will happen if he pushes or pulls the train?* (It will move.) *What are some different ways the train can move?* (straight, back and forth, in a circle) Read the sentence on side A of the card. Repeat with remaining cards.

Ask children the following questions:

- *What force makes the children on the swings slow down?* (friction)
- *What force makes the girl go down the slide?* (gravity)
- *How do you know the swings are in motion?* (They are moving back and forth.)
- *What is a force?* (a push or pull)

Explore and Learn

Inquiry Activity *Small group activity*

Model the Activity

- Place the materials for Activity Placemat 16 on each table, including copies of Activity Record Sheet 16 (p. 94).
- Model the correct pronunciation for each of the activity materials. Have children repeat the words.
- Read the steps of Activity Placemat 16 (Explore Friction) aloud with children. Model for children the correct way to rub the pieces of paper together.
- Guide children as they work in small groups to complete the activity and Activity Record Sheet 16. Caution children to carefully handle the sandpaper.
- Have each child work with a partner to complete the **Now Try This** activity.

Discuss the Activity

Invite children to discuss the activity and compare observations. Ask:

- *Which kind of paper is the roughest?*
- *Which kind of paper is the smoothest?*
- *What kind of force happened when you rubbed the pieces of paper together?*
- *Which kind of paper warmed your hands the most when you rubbed pieces of it together?*
- *Which kind of paper warmed your hands the least when you rubbed pieces of it together?*

Vocabulary Words
force, friction, gravity, motion

Science Objectives
Children will:
- define force
- describe how the roughness of a surface affects friction
- explain how friction and gravity affect an object's motion
- describe how motion can vary

TESOL/LA Objectives
Children will:
- understand and produce technical vocabulary
- use contextual clues
- follow oral and written directions
- record observations

Materials
- Concept Poster 6
- Science Vocabulary Cards 55–58
- Activity Placemat 16
- Activity Record Sheet 16
- Science Journal
- Science Content Picture Dictionary
- Flip Book Lesson 16
- Concept Web 16
- Radius™ Science Vocabulary Cards 55–58
- Transparency 16
- Lesson Review 16

Vocabulary Word Wall

Place these words on the Word Wall:

force, friction, gravity, motion

Have children copy the words in their Science Journals. Next, have children draw a picture to illustrate each word. Photocopy and post the children's illustrations below the appropriate words on the Word Wall.

Cognates

For Spanish-speaking children, it may be helpful to post this cognate chart to show similarities between words in Spanish and English. Keep in mind that children have varying literacy levels in Spanish, and some may not be familiar with these words.

Cognates	
English	**Spanish**
force	fuerza
friction	fricción
gravity	gravedad
motion	movimiento
paper	papel

Science Content Picture Dictionary

For children needing additional help with vocabulary words, refer them to the Science Content Picture Dictionary.

Explain Concepts and Vocabulary

Flip Book *Whole group activity*

Build Background

Review the Concept Poster 6 activity from the **Engage** section. Ask:

- *How does force affect things on the playground?*
- *How does friction affect things on the playground?*
- *How does gravity affect things on the playground?*
- *Which things in the playground are in motion?*

Read Flip Book, Lesson 16

- Point to the title and read it aloud. Have children repeat the words. Then ask children to brainstorm answers to the title question. If a child uses the word **force,** point to the word on the Flip Book page.
- Read the first sentence, pointing to each word as you read. Have children repeat the words. Point to the middle photo and say: *This photo shows some girls ice skating together.* Read the caption and have children repeat the words. Then ask: *What are the girls doing if they are in motion?* (moving) *What are some ways the girls might move?* (in a circle, back and forth)
- Read the second sentence, pointing to each word as you read. Have children repeat the words. Point to the photo on the left and say: *A force is acting on this ice skater.* Read the caption and have children repeat the words. Then ask: *How does friction affect the skater?* (Friction is pushing against her skates. It can slow down her motion.) Explain to children that friction acts in the direction that is opposite to that of a moving object.
- Point to the photo on the right and say: *A force is acting on this sled.* Read the caption and have children repeat the words. Then ask: *How is gravity acting on the sled?* (Gravity is pulling on it.)

Make Connections

- Point to the **Make Connections** box and read the statement. Then, as a whole group, discuss the motion in each picture. Ask: *How is the race car moving on the race track?* (The car is moving fast in a circle.) *How is the cheetah moving across the ground?* (The cheetah is running fast in a straight line.) *How are the boy and the ball moving?* (The boy is kicking a ball forward.)

Elaborate

Concept Web *Paired activity*

Distribute copies of Concept Web 16 (p. 95). Have each child work with a partner to complete the concept web. For children needing additional help with the web, refer them to the Concept Poster 6, Science Vocabulary Cards 55–58, and the Flip Book. When children have finished, ask volunteers to share and talk about their completed webs.

Radius™ Science Vocabulary Cards

Small group activity

Have children use the Radius™ Audio Learning System and Radius™ Science Vocabulary Cards 55–58 to practice listening to, reading, writing, and speaking each word. Then have children do one or more of the following activities in their Science Journals:

- Have children look in magazines and newspapers for pictures that illustrate the vocabulary words: force, friction, gravity, motion. Tell them to cut out the pictures and paste them into their Science Journals. Then have them use the vocabulary words as labels in their pictures. For example, children might find a picture of a basketball falling through a hoop to go with *motion* and *gravity.*

- Encourage children to think about sports they have played or watched. Tell them that force is involved in sports. Ask them to write sentences describing how force is used in some popular sports. Write completion sentences such as these on the board for children to write and complete: The batter uses force to _____ a _____. The kicker uses force to _____ a _____.

- Ask children to look for things in the classroom or outside that are in motion. Have them work with a partner to write a list of things in motion.

Evaluate

Transparency 16 *Whole group activity*

Assess Vocabulary Knowledge

Use side B (definition side) of the Science Vocabulary Cards 55–58 to review the lesson vocabulary words. Then distribute a copy of Transparency 16 to each child. Have children cut out the vocabulary words at the bottom of the page and place them in the correct boxes. Model the task for them by using Transparency 16. Invite volunteers to use each vocabulary word in a sentence.

Lesson Review 16 *Individual activity*

Assess Concept Knowledge

Distribute copies of Lesson Review 16 (p. 96). Read the directions aloud and verify children's understanding. For children whose literacy skills are emerging, consider reading the sentences aloud. When finished, review the correct answers with children.

Home Connection

Send the completed copy of Activity Record Sheet 16 (p. 94) home with each child to share with his or her family.

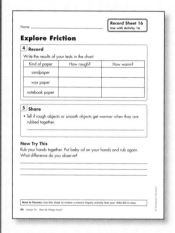

Send a second copy of Transparency 16 home with each child for extra review and practice. Encourage children to work with family members to cut out and place vocabulary words in the appropriate places on the transparency copy. Children can use the transparency copy to review vocabulary words throughout the school year.

Explore Friction

4 Record

Write the results of your tests in the chart.

Kind of paper	How rough?	How warm?
sandpaper		
wax paper		
notebook paper		

5 Share

• Tell if rough objects or smooth objects get warmer when they are rubbed together.

_____

Now Try This

Rub your hands together. Put baby oil on your hands and rub again. What difference do you observe?

_____

_____

_____

Note to Parents: Use this sheet to review a science inquiry activity that your child did in class.

Concept Web 16

Write the word from the box below that completes each sentence.

force	friction	gravity	motion

A _____
is a push or pull.

_____
is when something
moves from place to place.

_____
is a force that pulls
matter toward the
center of Earth.

_____
is a force that stops
or slows down
moving things that
touch each other.

Lesson Review 16

Write the word from the box that completes each sentence.

force	friction	motion	gravity

1. A force that pulls things to Earth is _____ .

2. A push or a pull is a _____ .

3. A force that makes moving things slow down is

_____ .

4. You use force to put an object in _____ .

Engage
Concept Poster 6 and Science Vocabulary
Cards 59–62 *Whole group activity*

Build Background
Show children side A of card 59 (magnetic force) and ask them to find a similar image on the poster. (toy train) Place card 59, image side out, in the pocket closest to the image. Say: *When the boy pulls on the train cars, they pull together. The train cars have magnets on them. If the boy turns one of the cars around, train cars push apart.* Ask: *What causes the pulling and pushing?* (a force in the magnets) Read the sentence on side A of the card. Repeat with card 60 (pole), card 61 (attract), and card 62 (repel). Ask children the following questions:

* *What has a north pole and a south pole?* (a magnet)
* *What do unlike poles of a magnet do?* (attract)
* *What do like poles of a magnet do?* (repel)
* *What kind of force does a magnet have?* (magnetic force)

Explore and Learn
Inquiry Activity *Small group activity*

Model the Activity
* Place the materials for Activity Placemat 17 on each table, including copies of Activity Record Sheet 17 (p. 100).
* Model the correct pronunciation for each of the activity materials (iron nail, paper clips, bar magnet). Have children repeat the words.
* Read the steps of Activity Placemat 17 (Make a Magnet) aloud with children. Model for children the correct way to rub the nail with a pole of the bar magnet.
* Guide children as they work in small groups to complete the activity and Activity Record Sheet 17. Caution children to carefully handle the nail.
* Have each child work with a partner to complete the **Now Try This** activity.

Discuss the Activity
Invite children to discuss the activity and compare observations. Ask:
* *In step 1, did the nail attract paper clips? What does this tell you about the nail?*
* *In step 4, did the nail attract paper clips? What does this tell you about the nail?*
* *What happened when you rubbed the bar magnet along the nail more times?*

Vocabulary Words
magnetic force, pole, attract, repel

Science Objectives
Children will:
* observe how magnets can pull or push objects
* show that magnetic force exists
* construct a magnet by magnetizing a nail
* describe the ways in which poles of magnets act toward each other

TESOL/LA Objectives
Children will:
* understand and produce technical vocabulary
* use contextual clues
* follow oral and written directions
* record observations
* compare objects

Materials
* Concept Poster 6
* Science Vocabulary Cards 59–62
* Activity Placemat 17
* Activity Record Sheet 17
* Science Journal
* Science Content Picture Dictionary
* Flip Book Lesson 17
* Concept Web 17
* Radius™ Science Vocabulary Cards 59–62
* Transparency 17
* Lesson Review 17

Explain Concepts and Vocabulary
Flip Book *Whole group activity*

Build Background

Review the Concept Poster 6 activity from the **Engage** section. Ask:
- *What can magnetic force do?*
- *What kinds of poles does every magnet have?*
- *What kind of poles of a magnet attract?*
- *What kind of poles of a magnet repel?*

Read Flip Book, Lesson 17

- Point to the title and read it aloud. Have children repeat the words. Then ask children to brainstorm answers to the title question. If a child uses the words **magnetic force,** point to the words on the Flip Book page.
- Read the first sentence, pointing to each word as you read. Have children repeat the words. Point to the train photo and say: *A force pulls these train cars together.* Read the caption and have children repeat the words. Then ask: *What is the force that pulls the train cars together?* (magnetic force) *What makes this magnetic force?* (magnets on the train cars)
- Read the second sentence, pointing to each word as you read. Have children repeat the words. Point to the photo of the magnet on the top of the page and say: *The two ends of a magnet are called poles.* Read the caption and have children repeat the words. Then ask: *What are the two poles of a magnet?* (north pole and south pole) *What does N stand for on a magnet?* (north pole) *What does S stand for on a magnet?* (south pole)
- Point to the photo of the two magnets attracting each other and say: *Magnetic force pulls these magnets together.* Read the caption and have children repeat the words. Then ask: *What is another name for "pull"?* (attract) *What unlike poles attract each other?* (the N pole on the magnet on the left and the S pole on the magnet on the right)
- Point to the photo of the two magnets repelling each other and say: *Magnetic force pushes these magnets away from each other.* Read the caption and have children repeat the words. Then ask: *What is another name for "push"?* (repel) *What like poles repel?* (the N poles of the two magnets)

Make Connections

- Point to the **Make Connections** box and read the statement aloud. Then, as a whole group, decide whether the magnets in each group would attract or repel each other. Ask: *Will the magnets in A attract or repel each other?* (attract) *How do you know?* (Unlike poles attract each other.) Repeat the procedure for B, C, and D.

Elaborate

Concept Web *Paired activity*

Distribute copies of Concept Web 17 (p. 101). Have each child work with a partner to complete the concept web. For children needing additional help with the web, refer them to the Concept Poster 6, Science Vocabulary Cards 59–62, and the Flip Book. When children have finished, ask volunteers to share and talk about their completed webs.

Radius™ Science Vocabulary Cards
Small group activity

Have children use the Radius™ Audio Learning System and Radius™ Science Vocabulary Cards 59–62 to practice listening to, reading, writing, and speaking each word. Then have children do one or more of the following activities in their Science Journals:

- Have children write this title: Words with Opposite Meanings. Then ask children to look for words on the Flip Book page that have opposite meanings and to list them below the title. (Words with opposite meanings include push and pull, attract and repel, north pole and south pole, and like and unlike.)

- Remind children that magnetic force is a force that pulls objects that contain iron. Give children a bar magnet and have them test objects in the classroom to see if a magnet attracts them. Tell children that the objects the magnet attracts have iron in them. Have children draw pictures of objects attracted to the magnet. Then have them write and complete this sentence: A _____ can pull these objects because they have iron.

- Encourage children to illustrate ways they have used magnets or have seen magnets being used. For example, some games, toys, tools, and machines use magnets. Help the children write a caption for each of their illustrations.

Evaluate

Transparency 17 *Whole group activity*

Assess Vocabulary Knowledge

Use side B (definition side) of the Science Vocabulary Cards 59–62 to review the lesson vocabulary words. Then distribute a copy of Transparency 17 to each child. Have children cut out the vocabulary words at the bottom of the page and place them in the correct boxes. Model the task for them by using Transparency 17. Invite volunteers to use each vocabulary word in a sentence.

Lesson Review 17 *Individual activity*

Assess Concept Knowledge

Distribute copies of Lesson Review 17 (p. 102). Read the directions aloud and verify children's understanding. For children whose literacy skills are emerging, consider reading the sentences aloud. When finished, review the correct answers with children.

Home Connection

Send the completed copy of Activity Record Sheet 17 (p. 100) home with each child to share with his or her family.

Send a second copy of Transparency 17 home with each child for extra review and practice. Encourage children to work with family members to cut out and place vocabulary words in the appropriate places on the transparency copy. Children can use the transparency copy to review vocabulary words throughout the school year.

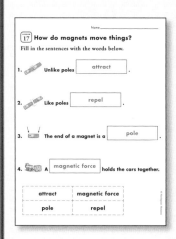

Make a Magnet

4 **Explore**

• Draw your nail picking up paper clips.

5 **Share**

• Tell how many paper clips your nail magnet picked up.

_____

Now Try This

Will rubbing the bar along the nail more times make the nail
magnet stronger? Try it!

Prediction: _____

Results: _____

Note to Parents: Use this sheet to review a science inquiry activity that your child did in class.

Concept Web 17

Fill in the blanks to write the vocabulary words.

A ___agnetic ___orce can
push or pull objects.

A ___ole is at the end
of a magnet.

Unlike poles ___ttract.

Like poles ___epe___.

Lesson Review 17

The picture shows a bar magnet.

| N | S |

1. Circle the magnet's poles.

2. Put an X on the magnet where magnetic force is strongest.

Circle the word that completes each sentence.

3. Unlike poles of two magnets _____ each other.

attract   **repel**

4. Like poles of two magnets _____ each other.

attract   **repel**

Engage

Concept Poster 7 and Science Vocabulary Cards 63–65 *Whole group activity*

Build Background

Show children side A of card 63 (energy) and ask them to find a similar image on the poster. (fire) Place card 63, image side out, in the pocket closest to the image. Ask: *What does this picture show?* (a fire) *What do we use fire for?* (to cook and for heat) Read the sentence on side A of the card. Repeat with card 64 (light) and card 65 (reflect).

Ask children the following questions:

- *What can the energy of a fire do?*
- *What are some things in the poster that give off light?*
- *What does light from the flashlight reflect off of?*

Explore and Learn

Inquiry Activity *Small group activity*

Model the Activity

- Place the materials for Activity Placemat 18 on each table, including copies of Activity Record Sheet 18 (p. 106).
- Model the correct pronunciation for each of the activity materials (white crayon, black paper, scissors, straw, tape, flashlight). Have children repeat the words.
- Read the steps of Activity Placemat 18 (Explore Light) aloud with children.
- Guide children as they work in small groups to complete the activity and Activity Record Sheet 18. Help them move the flashlight to show how the shadow changes.
- Have each child work with a partner to complete the **Now Try This** activity.

Discuss the Activity

Invite children to discuss the activity and compare observations. Ask:

- *What happened to the shadow when you held the flashlight closer? What happened to the shadow when you held the flashlight farther away?*
- *What happened to the shadow when you held the flashlight to the left and to the right?*
- *How did different lights change your shadow?*

Vocabulary Words

energy, light, reflect

Science Objectives

Children will:

- describe what energy does
- tell what light is and name some sources of light
- tell how light reflects
- describe how shadows form and change shape
- record observations and interpret them

TESOL/LA Objectives

Children will:

- understand and produce technical vocabulary
- use contextual clues
- explain actions
- record observations
- follow oral and written directions
- compare and contrast information

Materials

- Concept Poster 7
- Science Vocabulary Cards 63–65
- Activity Placemat 18
- Activity Record Sheet 18
- Science Journal
- Science Content Picture Dictionary
- Flip Book Lesson 18
- Concept Web 18
- Radius™ Science Vocabulary Cards 63–65
- Transparency 18
- Lesson Review 18

Explain Concepts and Vocabulary
Flip Book *Whole group activity*

Build Background
Review the Concept Poster 7 activity from the **Engage** section. Ask:
- *What is light?*
- *What are some things that give off light?*
- *What happens when light reflects off of an object?*

Read Flip Book, Lesson 18
- Point to the title and read it aloud. Have children repeat the words. Then ask children to brainstorm answers to the title question. If a child uses the words **fire, fireflies, lantern,** or **flashlight,** point to the images on the Flip Book page.
- Read the first sentence, pointing to each word as you read. Have children repeat the words. Point to the illustration and ask: *What are some examples of matter?* (the tent, the ground, the people, the air, etc.)
- Read the second sentence, pointing to each word as you read. Have children repeat the words. Point to the illustration and say: *Some things in the picture give off light.* Ask: *What do you see that gives off light?* (lantern, fire, flashlight, fireflies) *What is light?* (a kind of energy)
- Point to the drawing of the fire and read the caption. Have children repeat the words. Point out the fireflies. Say: *Fireflies are insects.* Ask: *What are the fireflies doing?* (giving off light)
- Point to the drawing of the girl reading and read the caption. Have children repeat the words. Ask: *What does the light from the flashlight do?* (It reflects from the book to the girl's eyes.) Ask: *What does the light from the lantern reflect off of?* (the tent and the area outside) *What does the light from the fire reflect off of?* (the tent and the people)

Make Connections
- Point to the **Make Connections** box and read the question aloud. Then, as a whole group, name the things shown. (firefly, flashlight, Sun, rocks) Ask: *Which objects make light?* (firefly, flashlight, Sun) *Which objects do not make light?* (rocks)

Elaborate

Concept Web *Paired activity*

Distribute copies of Concept Web 18 (p. 107). Have each child work with a partner to complete the concept web. For children needing additional help with the web, refer them to the Concept Poster 7, Science Vocabulary Cards 63–65, and the Flip Book. Then have them draw a picture of light reflecting off an object. When children have finished, ask volunteers to share and talk about their completed webs.

Radius™ Science Vocabulary Cards

Small group activity

Have children use the Radius™ Audio Learning System and Radius™ Science Vocabulary Cards 63–65 to practice listening to, reading, writing, and speaking each word. Then have children do one or more of the following activities in their Science Journals:

- Have children draw pictures that show what the energy from a fire does to water, meat, and wood. Then have them write a caption for each picture.
- Give children a list of other things that give off light: the Sun, stars, a lightbulb, a flashlight, a lantern, a fire. Have them draw a scene that includes at least three of these objects. Then have them label each object.
- Tell children that the Moon reflects light from the Sun. Ask children to draw a picture of a night scene showing the Moon. Then have them write a caption telling how we see the Moon.
- Invite children to use their own words to write definitions of the vocabulary words. Have them illustrate their definitions.

Evaluate

Transparency 18 *Whole group activity*

Assess Vocabulary Knowledge

Use side B (definition side) of the Science Vocabulary Cards 63–65 to review the lesson vocabulary words. Then distribute a copy of Transparency 18 to each child. Have children cut out the words at the bottom of the page and place them in the correct boxes. Model the task for them by using Transparency 18. Invite volunteers to use each vocabulary word in a sentence.

Lesson Review 18 *Individual activity*

Assess Concept Knowledge

Distribute copies of Lesson Review 18 (p. 108). Read the directions aloud and verify children's understanding. For children whose literacy skills are emerging, consider reading the sentences aloud. When finished, review the correct answers with children.

Home Connection
Send the completed copy of Activity Record Sheet 18 (p. 106) home with each child to share with his or her family.

Send a second copy of Transparency 18 home with each child for extra review and practice. Encourage children to work with family members to cut out and place vocabulary words in the appropriate places on the transparency copy. Children can use the transparency copy to review vocabulary words throughout the school year.

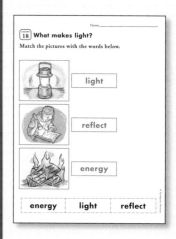

Explore Light

5 Record and Share

Write, draw, or talk about how your shadow changed.

• Tell what you learned about shadows.

_____

_____

_____

_____

Now Try This

Use different kinds of lights to make your shadow.
Tell how your shadow changes.

_____

_____

_____

Note to Parents: Use this sheet to review a science inquiry activity that your child did in class.

Concept Web 18

Fill in the letters to complete the words. Then draw a picture of light reflecting off an object.

___nergy can make matter change or move.

Ligh___   ___eflects off of objects.

Name _____

Lesson Review 18

Write the word from the box that completes each sentence.

Energy	Light	reflects

1. _____ can make matter change or move.

2. Light from the flashlight _____ from the book to the girl's eye.

3. _____ is energy we can see.

Draw something that makes light.

Engage

Concept Poster 7 and Science Vocabulary
Card 66 *Whole group activity*

Build Background

Show children side A of card 66 (heat) and ask them to find a similar image on the poster. (the fire) Place card 66, image side out, in the pocket closest to the image. Say: *The fire burns the wood.* Ask: *Where does the heat move in the campfire?* (from the fire to the wood) Say: *On the card, people are cooking marshmallows.* Ask: *How does the heat move?* (from the fire to the marshmallows) Read the sentence on side A of the card. Ask children the following questions:

* *Why do you think the family built a fire?*
* *What gives off heat in the picture?*
* *What is in the chest near the woman?*
* *How does the heat move in the ice chest?*

Explore and Learn

Inquiry Activity *Small group activity*

Model the Activity

* Place the materials for Activity Placemat 19 on each table, including copies of Activity Record Sheet 19 (p. 112).
* Model the correct pronunciation for each of the activity materials (white paper, black paper, tape, thermometer). Have children repeat the words. Explain that the thermometers can be used to measure temperature, or how hot or cool objects are. The liquid moves up in the tube as the temperature gets warmer.
* Read the steps of Activity Placemat 19 (Explore Heat and Sunlight) aloud with children.
* Guide children as they work in small groups to complete the activity and Activity Record Sheet 19. Help children by pointing out the numbers along the side of the thermometers. Tell them to use the Celsius scale.
* Have each child work with a partner to complete the **Now Try This** activity.

Discuss the Activity

Invite children to discuss the activity and compare observations. Ask:

* *Was there a temperature change?*
* *Was the temperature change the same for both thermometers?*
* *Which thermometer had the highest temperature at the end of 5 minutes?*
* *How does color affect temperature?*

Vocabulary Word
heat

Science Objectives
Children will:
* name things that give off heat
* understand how heat moves from one object to another
* gather and organize materials to complete an activity
* use a thermometer to measure the temperature of objects
* predict how different colors will affect temperature

TESOL/LA Objectives
Children will:
* understand and produce technical vocabulary
* use contextual clues
* engage in a class discussion
* follow oral and written directions
* record observations
* explain changes

Materials
* Concept Poster 7
* Science Vocabulary Card 66
* Activity Placemat 19
* Activity Record Sheet 19
* Science Journal
* Science Content Picture Dictionary
* Flip Book Lesson 19
* Concept Web 19
* Radius™ Science Vocabulary Card 66
* Transparency 19
* Lesson Review 19

Vocabulary Word Wall

Place this word on the Word Wall:

heat

Have children copy the word in their Science Journals. Next, have children draw a picture to illustrate the word. Photocopy and post the children's illustrations below the appropriate word on the Word Wall.

Cognates

For Spanish-speaking children, it may be helpful to post this cognate chart to show similarities between words in Spanish and English. Keep in mind that children have varying literacy levels in Spanish, and some may not be familiar with these words.

Cognates	
English	**Spanish**
temperature	temperatura
thermometer	termómetro

Science Content Picture Dictionary

For children needing additional help with vocabulary words, refer them to the Science Content Picture Dictionary.

Explain Concepts and Vocabulary
Flip Book *Whole group activity*

Build Background

Review the Concept Poster 7 activity from the **Engage** section. Ask:
- *What kinds of things give off heat?*
- *How do we use heat?*

Read Flip Book, Lesson 19

- Point to the title and read it aloud. Have children repeat the words. Then ask children to brainstorm answers to the title question. If a child uses the word **heat,** point to the word on the Flip Book page.
- Read the first sentence, pointing to each word as you read. Have children repeat the words. Point to the photo on the left and say: *This is the fire.* Ask: *What else do you see in this picture?* (marshmallows on sticks) Read the caption and have children repeat the words. Then ask: *How does the heat move here?* (from the fire to the marshmallows)
- Read the second sentence, pointing to each word as you read. Have children repeat the words. Point to the photo of the girl by the oven and say: *This girl is helping with the baking. What is she doing?* (taking the muffin pan out of the oven) Read the caption and have children repeat the words. Ask: *Where does the heat come from?* (the oven) *How does the heat move?* (from the oven to the pan to the muffins)
- Point to the photo of the ice cubes and read the caption aloud. Have children repeat the words. Ask: *Which is warmer—the ice cubes or the child's hands? How does heat move?* (from the hands to the ice cubes)

Make Connections

- Point to the **Make Connections** box and read the statement aloud. Then, as a whole group, name the objects that make heat. (burners on the stove, lightbulb in the lamp, toaster)

Elaborate

Concept Web *Paired activity*

Distribute copies of Concept Web 19 (p. 113). Have each child work with a partner to complete the concept web. For children needing additional help with the web, refer them to the Concept Poster 7, Science Vocabulary Card 66, and the Flip Book. Have them draw pictures of things that make heat to complete the concept web. When children have finished, ask volunteers to share and talk about their completed webs.

Radius™ Science Vocabulary Cards

Small group activity

Have children use the Radius™ Audio Learning System and Radius™ Vocabulary Card 66 to practice listening to, reading, writing, and speaking each word. Then have children do one or more of the following activities in their Science Journals:

- Provide children with pictures of a variety of objects such as the Sun, a fireplace, a frozen juice bar, a rock, and a lightbulb. Have children work in pairs to order the pictures according to the amount of heat they give off. Then have them paste the pictures into their Science Journals in the order they identify. Have them label the correct ends of their sequence *Hottest* and *Coolest*.

- Ask pairs of children to brainstorm examples of heat moving in their classroom or at home. Have them choose one or more examples to illustrate. Then have them write a sentence describing how the heat moves in each example. Write on the board this model sentence for children to follow: Heat moves from the warmer ____ to the cooler ____.

Evaluate

Transparency 19 *Whole group activity*

Assess Vocabulary Knowledge

Use side B (definition side) of the Science Vocabulary Card 66 to review the lesson vocabulary word. Then distribute a copy of Transparency 19 to each child. Have children cut out the pictures at the bottom of the page and place them in the correct boxes. Model the task for them by using Transparency 19. Invite volunteers to use the vocabulary word in a sentence.

Lesson Review 19 *Individual activity*

Assess Concept Knowledge

Distribute copies of Lesson Review 19 (p. 114). Read the directions aloud and verify children's understanding. For children whose literacy skills are emerging, consider reading the sentences aloud. When finished, review the correct answers with children.

Home Connection
Send the completed copy of Activity Record Sheet 19 (p. 112) home with each child to share with his or her family.

Send a second copy of Transparency 19 home with each child for extra review and practice. Encourage children to work with family members to cut out and place pictures in the appropriate places on the transparency copy. Children can use the transparency copy to review vocabulary words throughout the school year.

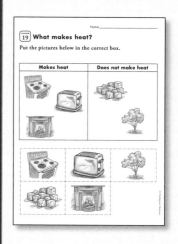

Explore Heat and Sunlight

4 Record

Put the temperatures you recorded in the chart.

Thermometer	Temperature	
	Step 2	Step 3
in white paper		
in black paper		

5 Share

• Talk about how color affects how hot an object gets when it is in sunlight._____

_____

Now Try This

How do you think other colors affect temperature? Make envelopes of other colors and find out.

Predictions: _____

_____

Results: _____

_____

_____

Note to Parents: Use this sheet to review a science inquiry activity that your child did in class.

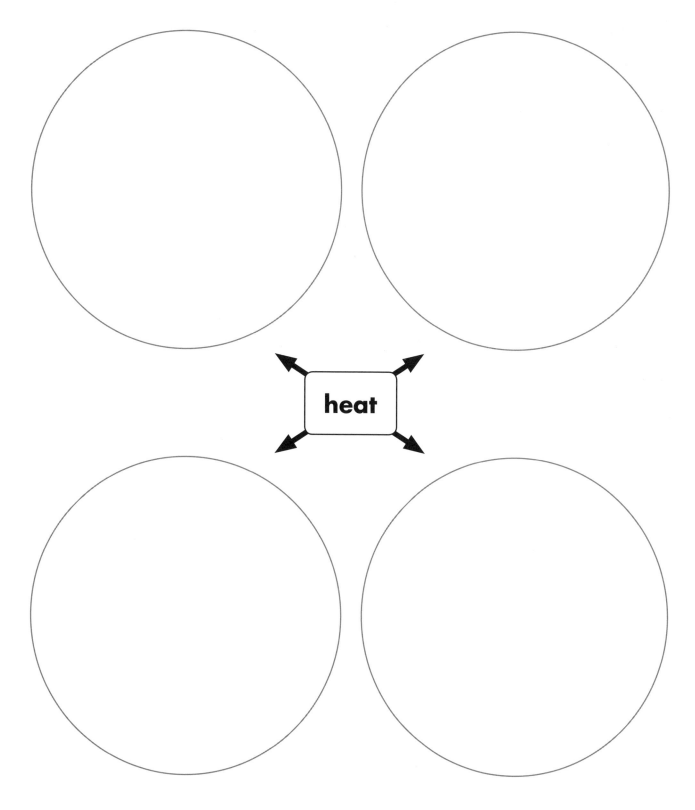

Name _____

Concept Web 19

Draw a picture in each circle to show things that make heat.

heat

Lesson Review 19

Circle the sentences that are TRUE about heat. Put a line through the sentence that is NOT true about heat.

1. Heat is a kind of matter.

2. A fire gives off heat.

3. Heat makes an object change temperature.

Draw two things that make heat.

What makes sound?

Engage

Concept Poster 7 and Science Vocabulary Cards 67–69 *Whole group activity*

Build Background

Show children side A of card 67 (vibrate) and ask them to find a similar image on the poster (guitar). Place card 67, image side out, in the pocket closest to the image. Say: *The man is playing a guitar. What part of the guitar vibrates?* (strings) Read the sentence on side A of the card. Ask: *When is a sound made?* (when something vibrates) Repeat with card 68 (loudness) and card 69 (pitch).

Ask children the following questions:

- *What other things in the picture vibrate to make sounds?*
- *How would you describe the sound the dog makes?*
- *How would you describe the pitch of the sound the drum makes?*
- *Do the waves make sounds? What is the loudness of the sounds made by different waves?*
- *What kinds of sound can a fire make?*

Explore and Learn

Inquiry Activity *Small group activity*

Model the Activity

- Place the materials for Activity Placemat 20 on each table, including copies of Activity Record Sheet 20 (p. 118).
- Model the correct pronunciation for each of the activity materials (cup, rubber band, plastic wrap, pepper, objects to make noise). Have children repeat the words. Explain that they will observe what causes sound.
- Read the steps of Activity Placemat 20 (Observe Sound) aloud with children.
- Guide children as they work in small groups to complete the activity and Activity Record Sheet 20. Help children make sure the plastic wrap on top of the cup is smooth.
- Have each child work with a partner to complete the **Now Try This** activity.

Discuss the Activity

Invite children to discuss the activity and compare observations. Ask:

- *What happened to the pepper when you clapped your hands?*
- *What happened when you made other noises near the top of the cup?*
- *Why did the pepper move?*
- *Did the pepper move more with some noises than it did with others? What do you think caused this?*

Vocabulary Words
vibrate, loudness, pitch

Science Objectives
Children will:
- identify what causes sound
- define loudness and pitch
- differentiate between loud and soft sounds
- differentiate between high-pitched and low-pitched sounds

TESOL/LA Objectives
Children will:
- understand and produce technical vocabulary
- use contextual clues
- follow oral and written directions
- compare and classify sounds
- record observations
- explain change

Materials
- Concept Poster 7
- Science Vocabulary Cards 67–69
- Activity Placemat 20
- Activity Record Sheet 20
- Science Journal
- Science Content Picture Dictionary
- Flip Book Lesson 20
- Concept Web 20
- Radius™ Science Vocabulary Cards 67–69
- Transparency 20
- Lesson Review 20

Explain Concepts and Vocabulary
Flip Book *Whole group activity*

Build Background

Review the Concept Poster 7 activity from the **Engage** section. Ask:

- *What happens when objects vibrate?*
- *Which things in the poster make sounds?*
- *Which sounds are loud? Which sounds are soft?*
- *Which sounds have a low pitch?*

Read Flip Book, Lesson 20

- Point to the title and read it aloud. Have children repeat the words. Then ask children to brainstorm answers to the title question. If a child uses the word **vibrate,** point to the word on the Flip Book page.
- Read the sentence, pointing to each word as you read. Have children repeat the words. Point to the photo at the top right and say: *Look at the guitar strings.* Read the caption and have children repeat the words. Then ask: *What do the guitar strings do when they vibrate?* (make a sound) *How do the strings move?* (quickly back and forth)
- Point to the next photo and say: *This wolf is howling.* Read the caption and have children repeat the words. Then ask: *Is the wolf's howl loud or soft?* (loud)
- Point to the photo of the girl. Say: *The girl is playing a drum.* Read the caption and have children repeat the words. Ask: *What is pitch?* (how high or low a sound is) *Does the drum have a high or low pitch?* (low) *Does a siren have a high or low pitch?* (high)

Make Connections

- Point to the **Make Connections** box. Then, as a whole group, decide what word is needed to complete the first sentence about the lawn mower. (loud) Repeat the process with the rest of the pictures. Ask: *What word would complete the sentence about falling leaves?* (soft) *What word would complete the sentence about the pitch of the whistle?* (high) *What word would complete the sentence about the pitch of the big drum?* (low)

Elaborate

Concept Web *Paired activity*

Distribute copies of Concept Web 20 (p. 119). Have each child work with a partner to complete the concept web. For children needing additional help with the web, refer them to the Concept Poster 7, Science Vocabulary Cards 67–69, and the Flip Book. Then have them draw pictures to illustrate the sentences. When children have finished, ask volunteers to share and talk about their completed webs.

Radius™ Science Vocabulary Cards
Small group activity

Have children use the Radius™ Audio Learning System and Radius™ Science Vocabulary Cards 67–69 to practice listening to, reading, writing, and speaking each word. Then have children do one or more of the following writing activities in their Science Journals:

- Invite children to make a "things that make sounds" alphabet, writing one word for each letter. Have children work with a partner to brainstorm words that they can use. Encourage them to use vocabulary words to write a sentence about each of their alphabet words.
- Have children make a two-column chart with heads that say *Loud Sounds* and *Soft Sounds.* Then have them work with a partner to write two sentences about things that make these sounds in each column.
- Use various objects in the classroom to make loud, soft, high, and low sounds. After you make each sound, have children work in small groups to write a sentence about the sound. Write a model sentence for children to follow on the board: The _____ makes a _____ sound.

Evaluate

Transparency 20 *Whole group activity*

Assess Vocabulary Knowledge

Use side B (definition side) of the Science Vocabulary Cards 67–69 to review the lesson vocabulary words. Then distribute a copy of Transparency 20 to each child. Have children cut out the pictures at the bottom of the page and place them in the correct box. Model the task for them by using Transparency 20. Invite volunteers to use each vocabulary word in a sentence.

Lesson Review 20 *Individual activity*

Assess Concept Knowledge

Distribute copies of Lesson Review 20 (p. 120). Read the directions aloud and verify children's understanding. For children whose literacy skills are emerging, consider reading the sentences aloud. When finished, review the correct answers with children.

Home Connection

Send the completed copy of Activity Record Sheet 20 (p. 118) home with each child to share with his or her family.

Send a second copy of Transparency 20 home with each child for extra review and practice. Encourage children to work with family members to cut out and place pictures in the appropriate places on the transparency copy. Children can use the transparency copy to review vocabulary words throughout the school year.

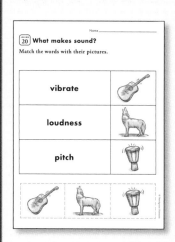

Observe Sound

5 Record and Share

Talk about what happened to the pepper with each sound.

Action	How action affected the pepper
Clap hands above cup.	

• Tell why the pepper moves.

_____

_____

• Tell how loudness affects the pepper.

_____

_____

Now Try This

Make the same sound near the cup and away from the cup.
Does the pepper move the same way each time?

_____

Note to Parents: Use this sheet to review a science inquiry activity that your child did in class.

© Northpoint Horizons™

Concept Web 20

Fill in the letters to complete each word. Then draw a picture of each sentence.

Guitar strings ___ibrate to make sounds.	
A wolf makes a lou___ sound when it howls.	
The ___itch of a whistle is high.	

Name _____

Lesson Review 20

**Write the word from the box that completes
each sentence.**

loudness	pitch	vibrates

1. The _____ of a sound is how loud
or soft it is.

2. A sound is made when something _____ .

3. A drum has a low _____ .

Draw something that makes sound.

What can you see in the day sky?

Engage

Concept Poster 8 and Science Vocabulary Cards 70–73 *Whole group activity*

Build Background

Show children side A of card 70 (Sun) and ask them to find a similar image on the poster (family group looking at a sunrise). Place card 70 image side out, in the pocket closest to the image. Ask: *What does the sky look like in the morning?* (It's light out.) *Where does the light come from?* (the Sun) Read the sentence on side A of the card. Repeat with remaining cards.

Ask children the following questions:

- *What can you see in the day sky?* (Sun, clouds, weather)
- *Where is the Sun in the morning?*
- *Does the Sun's position change during the day?*
- *What causes shadows?* (something blocking the light)
- *What is making shadows in the picture?* (trees, people)
- *How can you find out what kind of shadow an object makes?* (do an experiment)

Explore and Learn

Inquiry Activity *Small group activity*

Model the Activity

- Place the materials for Activity Placemat 21 on each table, including copies of Activity Record Sheet 21 (p. 124).
- Model the correct pronunciation for each of the activity materials (straw, clay, cardboard, stones, pencil, ruler). Have children repeat the words. Explain that they will use the straw and other materials to observe how shadows change during the day.
- Read the steps of Activity Placemat 21 (Observe How Shadows Change) aloud with children.
- Guide children as they work in small groups to complete the activity and Activity Record Sheet 21. Help children position the straw and clay where they can make observations throughout the day.
- Have each child work with a partner to complete the **Now Try This** activity.

Discuss the Activity

Invite children to discuss the activity and compare observations. Ask:

- *When was the line you drew the shortest? Where was the Sun?*
- *When was the line the longest? Where was the Sun?*
- *What happened to the length of the shadows throughout the day?*
- *Explain what made the length of the shadows change.*

Vocabulary Words
Sun, day, experiment, shadow

Science Objectives
Children will:
- name objects in the day sky
- explain why the length of shadows changes during the day
- interpret visual information
- record and interpret observations
- learn experimental methods

TESOL/LA Objectives
Children will:
- understand and produce technical vocabulary
- use contextual clues
- interpret and record visual information
- follow oral and written directions
- analyze, synthesize, and infer information

Materials
- Concept Poster 8
- Science Vocabulary Cards 70–73
- Activity Placemat 21
- Activity Record Sheet 21
- Science Journal
- Science Content Picture Dictionary
- Flip Book Lesson 21
- Concept Web 21
- Radius™ Science Vocabulary Cards 70–73
- Transparency 21
- Lesson Review 21

Vocabulary Word Wall

Place these words on the Word Wall:

Sun, day, experiment, shadow

Have children copy the words in their Science Journals. Next, have children draw a picture to illustrate each word. Photocopy and post the children's illustrations below the appropriate words on the Word Wall.

Cognates

For Spanish-speaking children, it may be helpful to post this cognate chart to show similarities between words in Spanish and English. Keep in mind that children have varying literacy levels in Spanish, and some may not be familiar with these words.

Cognates	
English	**Spanish**
day	día
experiment	experimento

Science Content Picture Dictionary

For children needing additional help with vocabulary words, refer them to the Science Content Picture Dictionary.

Explain Concepts and Vocabulary

Flip Book *Whole group activity*

Build Background

Review the Concept Poster 8 activity from the **Engage** section. Ask:

- *What is the man pointing at?*
- *What can you see in the sky in the picture?*
- *What objects form shadows in the picture?*
- *What makes the shadows form?*
- *How can you find out what objects form a shadow?*

Read Flip Book, Lesson 21

- Point to the title and read it aloud. Have children repeat the words. Then ask children to brainstorm answers to the title question. If a child uses any of the words **Sun, day, experiment,** or **shadow,** point to the words on the Flip Book page.
- Read the sentences, pointing to each word as you read. Have children repeat the words. Point to the light on the sidewalk. Say: *This is light.* Ask: *What makes the light?* (the Sun) *Where is the Sun?* (in the sky) *How can you tell it is day?* (You see light and shadows on the ground.)
- Point to the photo of the children. Say: *These children are doing an experiment with light and shadows.* Ask: *What is an experiment?* (a test) Read the caption about the experiment and have children repeat the words. Ask: *What is the girl doing?* (making shadows) *What is the boy doing?* (using chalk to trace the outline of the shadows) Read the caption alongside the girl and have children repeat the words. Ask: *Why can't you see shadows in the dark?* (Shadows are caused by things blocking light.) *What time was it when the photo was taken?* (3 P.M.) *How did the length of the shadows change?* (They got shorter until noon, and then the shadows lengthened.)

Make Connections

- Point to the **Make Connections** box and read the question aloud. Then, as a whole group, describe what is shown in each picture. (a boy playing soccer, a beach umbrella, a girl on the beach, a pear, and the shadows they make) Ask: *What makes the shadow in each picture?* (the objects and people blocking the sunlight)

Elaborate

Concept Web *Paired activity*

Distribute copies of Concept Web 21 (p. 125). Have each child work with a partner to complete the concept web. For children needing additional help with the web, refer them to the Concept Poster 8, Science Vocabulary Cards 70–73, and the Flip Book. Then have them draw a picture to illustrate each word. When children have finished, ask volunteers to share and talk about their completed webs.

Radius™ Science Vocabulary Cards
Small group activity

Have children use the Radius™ Audio Learning System and Radius™ Science Vocabulary Cards 70–73 to practice listening to, reading, writing, and speaking each word. Then have children do one or more of the following activities in their Science Journals:

- Ask children to draw a picture of the things they can see in the sky during the day. Have them label their pictures with vocabulary words.
- Have children draw a picture of someone or something casting a shadow. Tell them to include the Sun in their drawings. Have children work with a partner to write a caption telling what made the shadow form.
- Have small groups of children make shadow puppets by taping paper shapes to sticks. Dim the lights in the classroom, and have the groups make shadows on the wall using flashlights as light sources. Have children paste the puppets into their Science Journals. Tell children to write a sentence about the puppets telling what happened in the experiment.

Evaluate

Transparency 21 *Whole group activity*

Assess Vocabulary Knowledge

Use side B (definition side) of the Science Vocabulary Cards 70–73 to review the lesson vocabulary words. Then distribute a copy of Transparency 21 to each child. Have children cut out the vocabulary words at the bottom of the page and place them in the correct boxes. Model the task for them by using Transparency 21. Invite volunteers to use each vocabulary word in a sentence.

Lesson Review 21 *Individual activity*

Assess Concept Knowledge

Distribute copies of Lesson Review 21 (p. 126). Read the directions aloud and verify children's understanding. For children whose literacy skills are emerging, consider reading the sentences aloud. When finished, review the correct answers with children.

Home Connection

Send the completed copy of Activity Record Sheet 21 (p. 124) home with each child to share with his or her family.

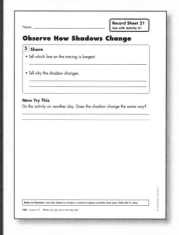

Send a second copy of Transparency 21 home with each child for extra review and practice. Encourage children to work with family members to cut out and place vocabulary words in the appropriate places on the transparency copy. Children can use the transparency copy to review vocabulary words throughout the school year.

Observe How Shadows Change

5 | **Share**

- Tell which line on the tracing is longest.

  _____

- Tell why the shadow changes.

  _____

  _____

Now Try This

Do the activity on another day. Does the shadow change the same way?

_____

_____

Note to Parents: Use this sheet to review a science inquiry activity that your child did in class.

Concept Web 21

Fill in the letters to complete each word. Then draw a picture of each vocabulary word.

___ay

___un

experimen___

sha___ow

Name _____

Lesson Review 21

Write the word from the box that completes each sentence.

day	experiment	Sun	shadow

1. The _____ gives light to Earth.

2. You see the Sun during the _____ .

3. A _____ is a dark shape made when something blocks light.

4. You can do an _____ to learn about light.

Engage

Concept Poster 8 and Science Vocabulary Cards 74–77 *Whole group activity*

Build Background

Show children side A of card 74 (night) and ask them to find a similar image on the poster (girl looking through a telescope). Place card 74, image side out, in the pocket closest to the image. Say: *What does the sky look like at night?* (It is dark.) *Can you see the Sun in the night sky?* (no) Read the sentence on side A of the card. Repeat with card 75 (Moon), card 76 (Moon phase), and card 77 (star).

Ask children the following questions:

- *What is the girl doing in the picture?* (looking through a telescope at the Moon and stars)
- *What shape is the Moon in the picture?* (crescent or part of a circle)
- *What are these Moon shapes called?* (Moon phases)
- *What different phases does the Moon show?* (full, half, quarter circle)
- *What else can you see in the sky in this part of the poster?*

Explore and Learn

Inquiry Activity *Small group activity*

Model the Activity

- Place the materials for Activity Placemat 22 on each table, including copies of Activity Record Sheet 22 (p. 130).
- Model the correct pronunciation for each of the activity materials (shoebox, clay, ball, flashlight). Have children repeat the words. Explain that they will use the ball and flashlight to model the Moon in the night sky.
- Read the steps of Activity Placemat 22 (Model the Night Sky) aloud with children.
- Guide children as they work in small groups to complete the activity and Activity Record Sheet 22. Help children position the ball and clay in the box so that the flashlight will shine on the ball.
- Have each child work with a partner to complete the **Now Try This** activity.

Discuss the Activity

Invite children to discuss the activity and compare observations. Ask:

- *What did you see when you looked without the light?*
- *What did you see with the light? What shape was it?*
- *Why can you see the Moon in the night sky?*
- *Why does the Moon's shape change?*

Vocabulary Words

night, Moon, Moon phase, star

Science Objectives

Children will:

- name objects seen in the night sky
- explain why the Moon's shape changes
- model how the Moon reflects sunlight and Moon phases form
- interpret visual information
- record observations and interpret those observations

TESOL/LA Objectives

Children will:

- understand and produce technical vocabulary
- use contextual clues
- participate in class discussions
- represent information visually and interpret information presented visually
- follow oral and written directions
- analyze, synthesize, and infer from information

Materials

- Concept Poster 8
- Science Vocabulary Cards 74–77
- Activity Placemat 22
- Activity Record Sheet 22
- Science Journal
- Science Content Picture Dictionary
- Flip Book Lesson 22
- Concept Web 22
- Radius™ Science Vocabulary Cards 74–77
- Transparency 22
- Lesson Review 22

Explain Concepts and Vocabulary

Flip Book *Whole group activity*

Build Background

Review the Concept Poster 8 activity from the **Engage** section. Ask:

- *What objects can you see in the sky at night?*
- *What Moon phase can be seen in the picture?*
- *Why would you use a telescope to look at the night sky?*

Read Flip Book, Lesson 22

- Point to the title and read it aloud. Have children repeat the words. Then ask children to brainstorm answers to the title question. If a child uses any of the words **night, Moon, Moon phase,** or **star,** point to the words on the Flip Book page.
- Read the sentence, pointing to each word as you read. Have children repeat the words. Point to the background picture of the night sky. Say: *It is night on this part of Earth. What is the sky like at night?* (very dark, black)
- Point to the Moon, and say: *This is the Moon.* Read the caption and have children repeat the words. Ask: *Why can we see the Moon?* (It reflects light from the Sun.) *How much of the Moon do you see here?* (the lighted half; a complete circle) *What is this Moon phase called?* (full Moon)
- Point to the inset picture of the Moon phases. Say: *These are the Moon phases.* Read the caption and have children repeat the words. Ask: *Why do we see different Moon phases?* (because we see different amounts of the lighted part of the Moon) *Does the Moon ever disappear completely from the night sky? When?* (yes, when the lighted part of the Moon is not facing Earth)
- Point to one of the stars and say: *This is a star.* Read the caption and have children repeat the words. Ask: *When do we see stars?* (in the night sky) *What star shines its light on Earth?* (the Sun)

Make Connections

- Point to the **Make Connections** box and read each statement aloud. Then, as a whole group, describe what is shown in each picture. Ask: *What can you tell about this night sky?* (The sky is dark; you can see the Moon and stars in the sky; the Moon has a curved shape.) *Why does the Moon's shape change?* (We see different parts of the lighted part of the Moon each night. These different shapes are called Moon phases.)

Elaborate

Concept Web *Paired activity*

Distribute copies of Concept Web 22 (p. 131). Have each child work with a partner to complete the concept web. For children needing additional help with the web, refer them to the Concept Poster 8, Science Vocabulary Cards 74–77, and the Flip Book. Then have them draw pictures to illustrate each word. When children have finished, ask volunteers to share and talk about their completed webs.

Radius™ Science Vocabulary Cards
Small group activity

Have children use the Radius™ Audio Learning System and Radius™ Science Cards 74–77 to practice listening to, reading, writing, and speaking each word. Then have children do one or more of the following activities in their Science Journals:

- Have children imagine that they are scientists looking at the night sky with a telescope. Have them draw a picture of what they might see. Have them label the objects visible in the night sky.
- Have children go outside with an adult at a time when the Moon is visible. Have them draw the shape of the Moon in their Science Journals each night for one week. Encourage them to write a sentence describing how the shape of the Moon changes.
- Have children draw pictures of a group of stars in the night sky. Have them share their drawings in small groups. Then have children write captions that tell about the stars in their pictures.

Evaluate

Transparency 22 *Whole group activity*

Assess Vocabulary Knowledge

Use side B (definition side) of the Science Vocabulary Cards 74–77 to review the lesson vocabulary words. Then distribute a copy of Transparency 22 to each child. Have children cut out the words at the bottom of the transparency and place them in the correct boxes. Model the task for them by using Transparency 22. Invite volunteers to use each vocabulary word in a sentence.

Lesson Review 22 *Individual activity*

Assess Concept Knowledge

Distribute copies of Lesson Review 22 (p. 132). Read the directions aloud and verify children's understanding. For children whose literacy skills are emerging, consider reading the sentences aloud. When finished, review the correct answers with children.

Home Connection

Send the completed copy of Activity Record Sheet 22 (p. 130) home with each child to share with his or her family.

Send a second copy of Transparency 22 home with each child for extra review and practice. Encourage children to work with family members to cut out and place vocabulary words in the appropriate places on the transparency copy. Children can use the transparency copy to review vocabulary words throughout the school year.

Model the Night Sky

3 Observe

Look through the hole at the short end of the box (no light).

• Draw what you see.

4 Explore

Look through the hole at the short end of the box (with light).

• Draw what you see.

5 Share

• Tell why you can see the Moon in the night sky.

_____

_____

Now Try This

Suppose the Sun were on the other side of the Moon. What would the Moon look like? Make another hole in the box and find out. Draw what you see.

Name _____

Concept Web 22

Fill in the letters to complete each word. Then draw a picture of each word.

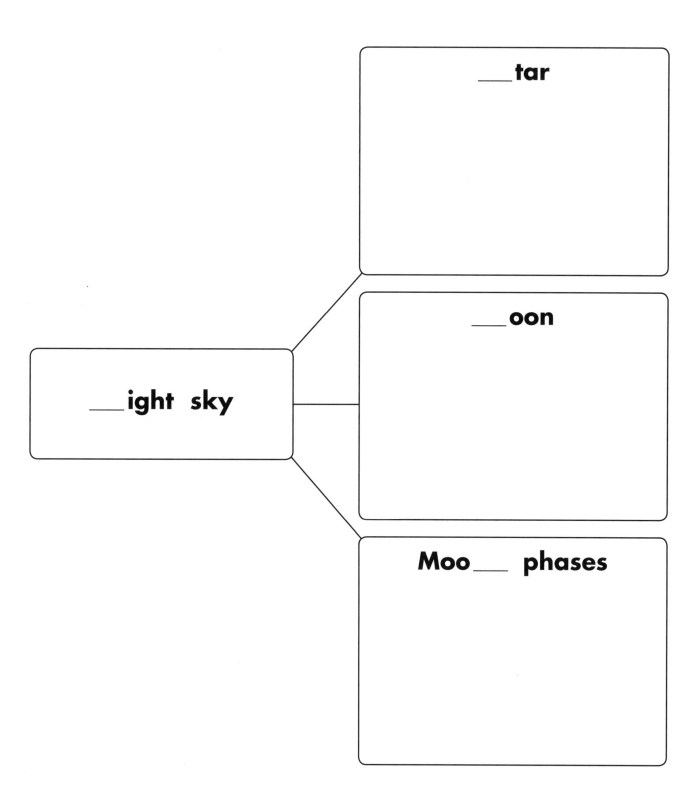

___tar

___oon

___ight sky

Moo___ phases

Lesson Review 22

Circle the word that completes each sentence.

1. _____ is when your part of Earth faces away from the Sun.

Night   **Day**

2. _____ reflects light from the Sun.

The Moon   **A star**

3. _____ is a hot ball of gas.

The Moon   **A star**

Draw pictures to show how the Moon phases change.

Engage

Concept Poster 8 and Science Vocabulary
Cards 78–80 *Whole group activity*

Build Background

Show children side A of card 78 (axis) and ask them to find a similar image on the poster. (Earth's axis) Place card 78, image side out, in the pocket closest to the image. Say: *Earth is not still in space. It is always moving. How does Earth move?* (Earth turns around and around.) Read the sentence on side A of the card. Repeat with card 79 (rotation) and card 80 (orbit).

Ask children the following questions:

* *What does Earth spin on?* (its axis)
* *How long does Earth's orbit around the Sun take?* (one year)
* *How long does Earth's rotation take?* (one day)

Explore and Learn

Inquiry Activity *Small group activity*

Model the Activity

* Place the materials for Activity Placemat 23 on each table, including copies of Activity Record Sheet 23 (p. 136).
* Model the correct pronunciation for each of the activity materials (goggles, foam ball, markers, pencil, flashlight). Have children repeat the words. Explain that the foam ball will model Earth and the pencil will model Earth's axis.
* Read the steps of Activity Placemat 23 (Explore the Causes of Seasons) aloud with children. Model the directions in step 1 for children.
* Guide children as they work in small groups to complete the activity and Activity Record Sheet 23. Caution children to be careful when working with the sharp pencil to prevent a puncture injury.
* Have each child work with a partner to complete the **Now Try This** activity.

Discuss the Activity

Invite children to discuss the activity and compare observations. Ask:

* *What are the seasons of the year on Earth called? What are the seasons like in our area?*
* *When does where you live on Earth get the most light from the Sun? What season is this?*
* *When does where you live on Earth get the least light from the Sun? What season is this?*

Vocabulary Words

axis, rotation, orbit

Science Objectives

Children will:

* describe Earth's rotation on its axis
* describe Earth's orbit around the Sun
* make models of Earth and the Sun
* model Earth's orbit around the Sun
* observe how Earth's tilt affects sunlight reaching Earth
* describe how the Sun and the movements of Earth cause seasons

TESOL/LA Objectives

Children will:

* understand and produce technical vocabulary
* follow oral written directions
* record observations
* analyze, synthesize and infer from information

Materials

* Concept Poster 8
* Science Vocabulary Cards 78–80
* Activity Placemat 23
* Activity Record Sheet 23
* Science Journal
* Science Content Picture Dictionary
* Flip Book Lesson 23
* Concept Web 23
* Radius™ Science Vocabulary Cards 78–80
* Transparency 23
* Lesson Review 23

Explain Concepts and Vocabulary

Flip Book *Whole group activity*

Build Background

Review the Concept Poster 8 activity from the **Engage** section. Ask:

- *What is Earth's axis?* (an imaginary line through Earth's center)
- *How long does it take Earth to make one orbit around the Sun?* (one year)
- *How often does Earth make one rotation?* (every day)

Read Flip Book, Lesson 23

- Point to the title and read it aloud. Have children repeat the words. Then ask children to brainstorm answers to the title question. If a child uses the words **axis, rotation,** or **orbit,** point to the word on the Flip Book page.
- Read the first sentence, pointing to each word as you read. Have children repeat the words. Point to the photo of Earth and say: *In this picture, Earth's axis looks like a red line through its center.* Ask: *What does Earth do on its axis?* (spins)
- Point to the arrow that shows Earth's rotation. Say: *The blue arrow shows how Earth spins on its axis.* Read the caption and have children repeat the words. Then ask: *What is a rotation?* (one whole spin on Earth's axis) *How long does it take for Earth to make one rotation?* (one day)
- Read the second sentence, pointing to each word as you read. Have children repeat the words. Point to the pictures of the Sun and Earth's orbit. Trace Earth's orbit continuously with a finger and say: *Earth moves in a path around the Sun.* Read the orbit caption and have children repeat the words. Then ask: *What is Earth's path around the Sun called?* (an orbit)

Make Connections

- Point to the **Make Connections** box and read the statement aloud. Have children look at the picture. Then, as a whole group, describe Earth's movements. Ask: *How is Earth moving on its axis?* (It is spinning on its axis.) *What is Earth moving around the Sun in?* (an orbit)

Elaborate

Concept Web *Paired activity*

Distribute copies of Concept Web 23 (p. 137). Have each child work with a partner to complete the concept web. For children needing additional help with the web, refer them to the Concept Poster 8, Science Vocabulary Cards 78–80, and the Flip Book. Then have them draw pictures of the vocabulary words to complete the web. When children have finished, ask volunteers to share and talk about their completed webs.

Radius™ Science Vocabulary Cards
Small group activity

Have children use the Radius™ Audio Learning System and Radius™ Science Vocabulary Cards 78–80 to practice listening to, reading, writing, and speaking each word. Then have children do one or more of the following activities in their Science Journals:

- Draw a picture on the board of Earth at four equidistant positions in orbit around the Sun. Make sure Earth's axis is always tilted in the same direction. Use an arrow to show how Earth rotates on it axis. Use arrows to show the direction Earth moves along its orbit. Tell children to draw a copy of the picture in their Science Journals. Then help children label Earth's positions as *winter, spring, summer,* and *autumn.* Have them caption their picture: Earth's movements cause the seasons.
- Have children draw the side of the school the Sun is on when they get to school in the morning. Then have them draw the side the Sun is on when they leave school in the afternoon. Explain to children that the Sun does not actually move. Earth's rotation makes the Sun appear to move in the sky. Tell children to caption their drawings: Earth's rotation makes the Sun seem to move east to west across the sky.

Evaluate

Transparency 23 *Whole group activity*

Assess Vocabulary Knowledge

Use side B (definition side) of the Science Vocabulary Cards 78–80 to review the lesson vocabulary words. Then distribute a copy of Transparency 23 to each child. Have children cut out the words at the bottom of the page and place them in the correct boxes. Model the task for them by using Transparency 23. Invite volunteers to use each vocabulary word in a sentence.

Lesson Review 23 *Individual activity*

Assess Concept Knowledge

Distribute copies of Lesson Review 23 (p. 138). Read the directions aloud and verify children's understanding. For children whose literacy skills are emerging, consider reading the sentences aloud. When finished, review the correct answers with children.

Home Connection
Send the completed copy of Activity Record Sheet 23 (p. 136) home with each child to share with his or her family.

Send a second copy of Transparency 23 home with each child for extra review and practice. Encourage children to work with family members to cut out and place vocabulary words in the appropriate places on the transparency copy. Children can use the transparency copy to review vocabulary words throughout the school year.

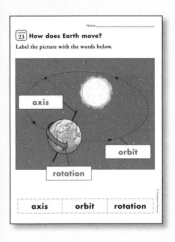

Explore the Causes of Seasons

5 Share

- Tell when the dot got the most light.

_____

_____

_____

_____

- Tell when the dot got the least light.

_____

_____

_____

_____

Now Try This

In which two places does the dot get the same amount of light?
Try the activity again to find out.

_____

_____

_____

_____

Note to Parents: Use this sheet to review a science inquiry activity that your child did in class.

Concept Web 23

Fill in the letters to complete each word. Then draw a picture of each word.

___xis	
___otation	
___rbi___	

Lesson Review 23

Write the words from the box that completes each sentence.

axis	orbit	rotation	Sun

1. Earth spins on its _____ .

2. One whole spin is called a _____ .

3. Earth moves around the _____ .

4. The path Earth takes is called an _____ .

Engage

Concept Poster 8 and Science Vocabulary
Cards 81–83 *Whole group activity*

Build Background

Show children side A of card 81 (planet) and ask them to find a similar image on the poster. (Earth) Place card 81, image side out, in the pocket closest to the image. Say: *These space objects orbit the Sun.* Ask: *What shape are they?* (round) *Are they all the same size?* (no) *Are they all the same distance from the Sun?* (no) Read the sentence on side A of the card. Repeat with card 82 (solar system) and card 83 (scientific methods). Ask children the following questions:

- *What is Earth?* (a planet)
- *How many planets do you see in our solar system?* (eight)
- *What do scientists use to answer questions about the solar system?* (scientific methods)

Explore and Learn

Inquiry Activity *Small group activity*

Model the Activity

- Place the materials for Activity Placemat 24 on each table, including copies of Activity Record Sheet 24 (p. 142).
- Model the correct pronunciation for each of the activity materials (colored paper, scissors, string and tape, hanger). Have children repeat the words. Explain that their model will show the Sun and planets in our solar system.
- Read the steps of Activity Placemat 24 (Model the Solar System) aloud with children.
- Guide children as they work in small groups to complete the activity and Activity Record Sheet 24. Demonstrate how to cut out the Sun and planets. Write the names of the planets in order from the Sun on the board (see Flip Book Lesson 24). Students can copy the names to label their planet models.
- Have each child work with a partner to complete the **Now Try This** activity.

Discuss the Activity

Invite children to discuss the activity and compare observations. Ask:
- *Which two planets are the largest in the solar system?*
- *Which two planets are the smallest in the solar system?*
- *What is the order of the planets from the Sun?*

Vocabulary Words
planet, solar system, scientific methods

Science Objectives
Children will:
- make models of the Sun and planets in our solar system
- name the planets in our solar system in order from the Sun

TESOL/LA Objectives
Children will:
- understand and produce technical vocabulary
- follow oral and written directions
- select, connect, and explain information

Materials
- Concept Poster 8
- Science Vocabulary Cards 81–83
- Activity Placemat 24
- Activity Record Sheet 24
- Science Journal
- Science Content Picture Dictionary
- Flip Book Lesson 24
- Concept Web 24
- Radius™ Science Vocabulary Cards 81–83
- Transparency 24
- Lesson Review 24

Vocabulary Word Wall

Place these words on the Word Wall:

planet, solar system, scientific methods

Have children copy the words in their Science Journals. Next, have children draw a picture to illustrate each word. Photocopy and post the children's illustrations below the appropriate words on the Word Wall.

Cognates

For Spanish-speaking children, it may be helpful to post this cognate chart to show similarities between words in Spanish and English. Keep in mind that children have varying literacy levels in Spanish, and some may not be familiar with these words.

Cognates	
English	**Spanish**
planet	planeta
solar system	sistema solar
Mercury	Mercurio
Venus	Venus
Mars	Marte
Jupiter	Júpiter
Saturn	Saturno
Uranus	Urano
Neptune	Neptuno

Science Content Picture Dictionary

For children needing additional help with vocabulary words, refer them to the Science Content Picture Dictionary.

Explain Concepts and Vocabulary

Flip Book *Whole group activity*

Build Background

Review the Concept Poster 8 activity from the **Engage** section. Ask:
- *What is our planet called?*
- *How many planets does our solar system have?*
- *Why do scientists use scientific methods?*

Read Flip Book, Lesson 24

- Point to the title and read it aloud. Have children repeat the words. Then ask children to brainstorm answers to the title question. If a child uses the words **solar system** or **planet,** point to the words on the Flip Book page.
- Read the first sentence, pointing to each word as you read. Have children repeat the words. Point to Earth in the picture of the solar system and say: *Earth orbits the Sun.* Read the label and have children repeat the word. Then ask: *What color does Earth look?* (blue)
- Read the second sentence, pointing to each word as you read. Have children repeat the words. Point to all of the planets in the photo of the solar system and say: *Eight planets orbit the Sun.* Read each of the planet labels in turn and have children repeat the words. Then ask: *How are the planets alike?* (They have the same shape and they orbit the Sun.) *How are they different?* (They are different sizes and different distances away from the Sun.)
- Point to the photo of the scientist and read the caption. Have children repeat the words. Ask: *What questions might a scientist ask about the solar system?* (Answers might include: Are there other objects in the solar system? What are these objects? Do these objects orbit the Sun?)

Make Connections

- Point to the **Make Connections** box and read the question and statement aloud. Have children look at the pictures. Then, as a whole group, discuss which pictures show planets and name them. (Left picture shows Saturn. Farthest right picture shows Earth.)

Elaborate

Concept Web *Paired activity*

Distribute copies of Concept Web 24 (p. 143). Have each child work with a partner to complete the concept web. For children needing additional help with the web, refer them to the Concept Poster 8, Science Vocabulary Cards 81–83, and the Flip Book. When children have finished, ask volunteers to share and talk about their completed webs.

Radius™ Science Vocabulary Cards
Small group activity

Have children use the Radius™ Audio Learning System and Radius™ Science Vocabulary Cards 81–83 to practice listening to, reading, writing, and speaking each word. Then have children do one or more of the following activities in their Science Journals:

- Have children draw pictures of Mercury, Venus, Mars, Jupiter, Saturn, Uranus, and Neptune. Then have them write a sentence that tells what these objects in the solar system are.
- Have children draw pictures that illustrate the vocabulary words *planet, solar system,* and *scientific methods* in their Science Journals. Then have them write the vocabulary words as labels for their pictures.
- Show children how to make a chart with eight columns. Label the columns *Mercury, Venus, Earth, Mars, Jupiter, Saturn, Uranus,* and *Neptune.* Children should write key words that refer to a particular planet in each column. For example, these key words might fit in the column labeled *Earth:* round, blue, orbit.

Evaluate

Transparency 24 *Whole group activity*

Assess Vocabulary Knowledge

Use side B (definition side) of the Science Vocabulary Cards 81–83 to review the lesson vocabulary words. Then distribute a copy of Transparency 24 to each child. Have children cut out the words at the bottom of the page and place them in the correct boxes. Model the task for them by using Transparency 24. Invite volunteers to use each vocabulary word in a sentence.

Lesson Review 24 *Individual activity*

Assess Concept Knowledge

Distribute copies of Lesson Review 24 (p. 144). Read the directions aloud and verify children's understanding. For children whose literacy skills are emerging, consider reading the sentences aloud. When finished, review the correct answers with children.

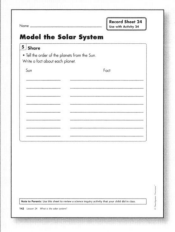
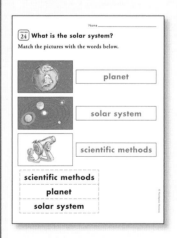

Name ______________________________

Record Sheet 24
Use with Activity 24

Model the Solar System

5 Share

- Tell the order of the planets from the Sun.

Write a fact about each planet.

Sun	Fact
______________	______________________________
______________	______________________________
______________	______________________________
______________	______________________________
______________	______________________________
______________	______________________________
______________	______________________________
______________	______________________________

Note to Parents: Use this sheet to review a science inquiry activity that your child did in class.

Concept Web 24

Fill in the letters to complete each word. Then draw a picture of each word.

___ **lane** ___

___ **olar** ___ **ystem**

___ **cientific** ___ **ethods**

Lesson Review 24

Circle the word that completes each sentence.

1. Earth is a _____ .

star   **planet**

2. There are _____ planets in our solar system.

eight   **ten**

3. The planets in our solar system travel around the _____ .

Sun   **Moon**

Draw a picture.

Show a scientist using scientific methods to answer a question about the solar system.

Concept Web Answer Key Lessons 1–4

Name

Concept Web 1

Fill in the blanks to write the vocabulary words. Draw a picture of each vocabulary word.

__l__iving __t__hing	__n__onliving thin__g__
Drawings may include deer, tree, fish, frog, bird, cattails, dandelion, etc.	Drawings may include rocks, soil, or water.

© Northpoint Horizons™

Lesson 1 *What are living things?* **5**

Concept Web 2

Draw pictures to show the life cycle of a plant. Write vocabulary words to name the pictures.

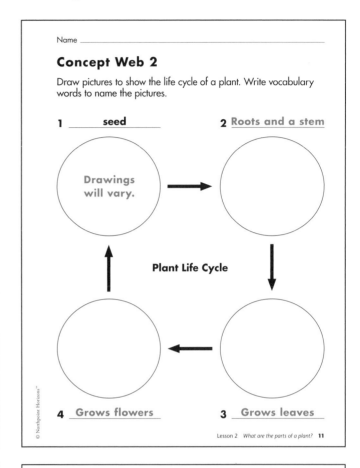

1 __seed__

2 __Roots and a stem__

Drawings will vary.

Plant Life Cycle

4 __Grows flowers__

3 __Grows leaves__

© Northpoint Horizons™

Lesson 2 *What are the parts of a plant?* **11**

Concept Web 3

Draw a picture for each kind of animal that has a backbone.

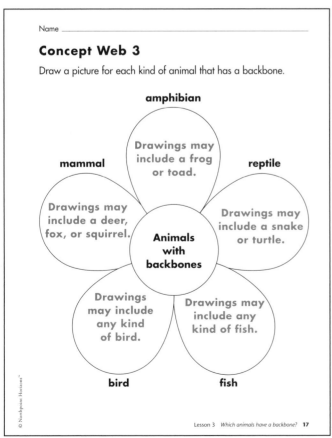

amphibian

Drawings may include a frog or toad.

mammal

Drawings may include a deer, fox, or squirrel.

reptile

Drawings may include a snake or turtle.

Animals with backbones

Drawings may include any kind of bird.

Drawings may include any kind of fish.

bird

fish

© Northpoint Horizons™

Lesson 3 *Which animals have a backbone?* **17**

Concept Web 4

Fill in the blanks to write words describing how a frog grows and changes. Draw a picture of each word.

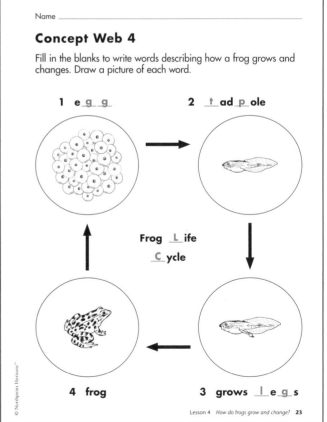

1 e __g__ __g__

2 __t__ ad __p__ ole

Frog __L__ ife __C__ ycle

4 frog

3 grows __l__ __e__ __g__ s

© Northpoint Horizons™

Lesson 4 *How do frogs grow and change?* **23**

Concept Web Answer Key Lessons 5–8

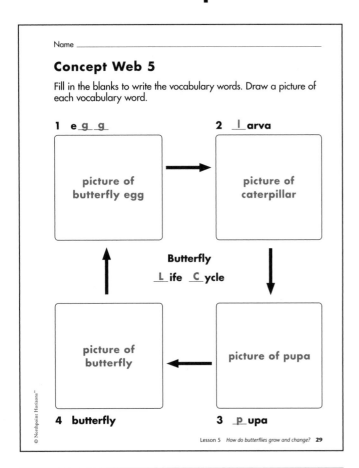

Name _____

Concept Web 5

Fill in the blanks to write the vocabulary words. Draw a picture of each vocabulary word.

1 e_g_ _g_

picture of butterfly egg

2 _l_ arva

picture of caterpillar

Butterfly
_L_ ife _C_ ycle

4 butterfly

picture of butterfly

3 _p_ upa

picture of pupa

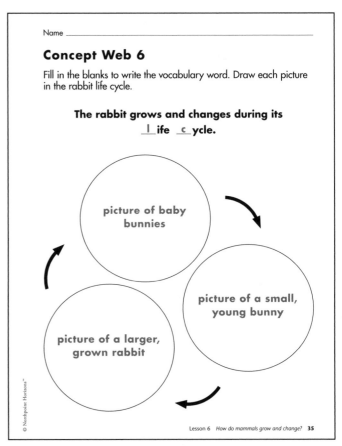

Name _____

Concept Web 6

Fill in the blanks to write the vocabulary word. Draw each picture in the rabbit life cycle.

The rabbit grows and changes during its
_l_ ife _c_ ycle.

picture of baby bunnies

picture of a small, young bunny

picture of a larger, grown rabbit

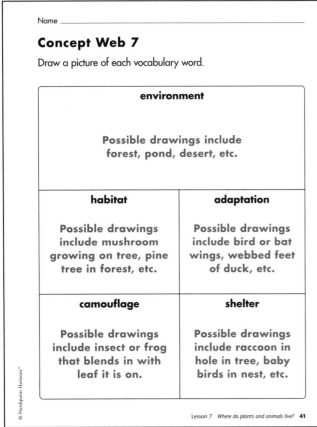

Name _____

Concept Web 7

Draw a picture of each vocabulary word.

environment	
Possible drawings include forest, pond, desert, etc.	
habitat	**adaptation**
Possible drawings include mushroom growing on tree, pine tree in forest, etc.	Possible drawings include bird or bat wings, webbed feet of duck, etc.
camouflage	**shelter**
Possible drawings include insect or frog that blends in with leaf it is on.	Possible drawings include raccoon in hole in tree, baby birds in nest, etc.

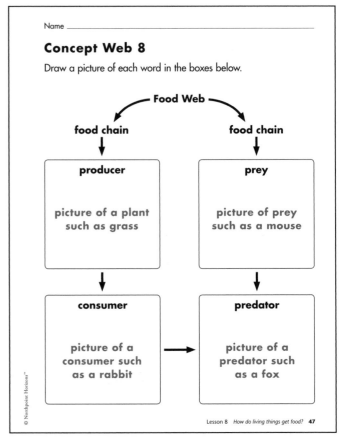

Name _____

Concept Web 8

Draw a picture of each word in the boxes below.

Food Web

food chain

food chain

producer

picture of a plant such as grass

prey

picture of prey such as a mouse

consumer

picture of a consumer such as a rabbit

predator

picture of a predator such as a fox

Concept Web Answer Key Lessons 9–12

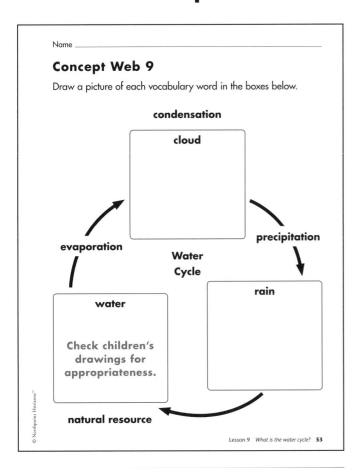

Name _____

Concept Web 9

Draw a picture of each vocabulary word in the boxes below.

condensation

cloud

evaporation

Water Cycle

precipitation

water

Check children's drawings for appropriateness.

rain

natural resource

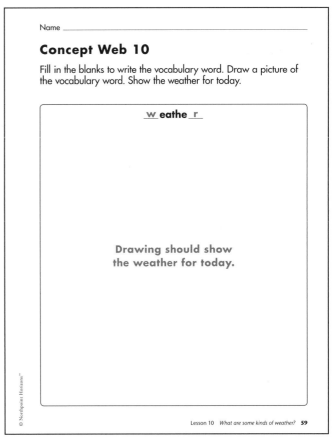

Name _____

Concept Web 10

Fill in the blanks to write the vocabulary word. Draw a picture of the vocabulary word. Show the weather for today.

<u>w</u> eathe <u>r</u>

Drawing should show the weather for today.

Name _____

Concept Web 11

Fill in the blanks to write the vocabulary words. Draw a picture of each vocabulary word.

1. <u>W</u> eatherin <u>g</u> is when living things, water, or wind breaks rocks.

Check children's drawings for appropriateness.

2. <u>E</u> rosio <u>n</u> is when wind or water moves soil or rock.

3. <u>P</u> ollutio <u>n</u> harms living things.

Name _____

Concept Web 12

Draw a picture of each season.

Spring	**Summer**
Drawings may include flowers and trees with buds or new leaves.	Drawings may include children swimming or trees with full leaves.
Autumn	**Winter**
Drawings may include a tree with colored leaves or children playing in leaves.	Drawings may include snow and ice or a bare tree.

Concept Web Answer Key Lessons 13–16

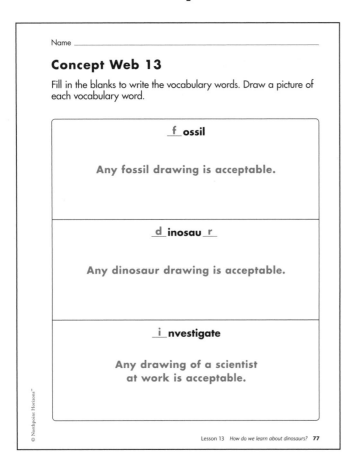

Name _____

Concept Web 13

Fill in the blanks to write the vocabulary words. Draw a picture of each vocabulary word.

__f_ ossil

Any fossil drawing is acceptable.

__d_ inosau __r_

Any dinosaur drawing is acceptable.

__i_ nvestigate

Any drawing of a scientist at work is acceptable.

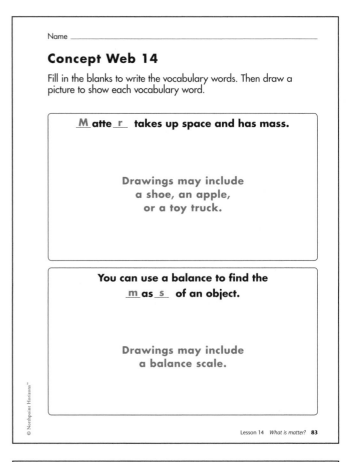

Name _____

Concept Web 14

Fill in the blanks to write the vocabulary words. Then draw a picture to show each vocabulary word.

__M_ atte __r_ takes up space and has mass.

Drawings may include a shoe, an apple, or a toy truck.

You can use a balance to find the __m_ as __s_ of an object.

Drawings may include a balance scale.

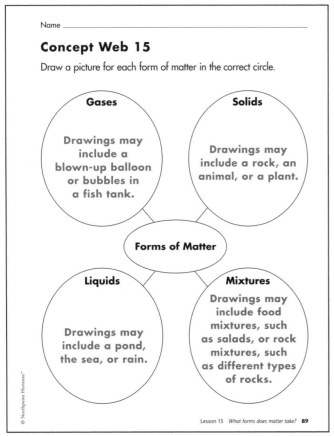

Name _____

Concept Web 15

Draw a picture for each form of matter in the correct circle.

Gases
Drawings may include a blown-up balloon or bubbles in a fish tank.

Solids
Drawings may include a rock, an animal, or a plant.

Forms of Matter

Liquids
Drawings may include a pond, the sea, or rain.

Mixtures
Drawings may include food mixtures, such as salads, or rock mixtures, such as different types of rocks.

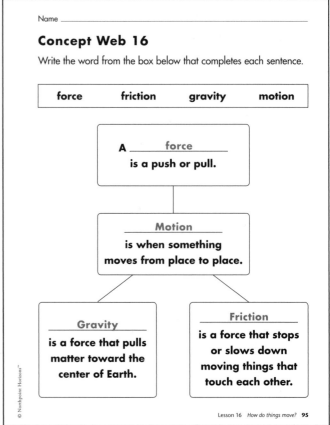

Name _____

Concept Web 16

Write the word from the box below that completes each sentence.

| force | friction | gravity | motion |

A ___force___
is a push or pull.

___Motion___
is when something moves from place to place.

___Gravity___
is a force that pulls matter toward the center of Earth.

___Friction___
is a force that stops or slows down moving things that touch each other.

Concept Web Answer Key Lessons 17–20

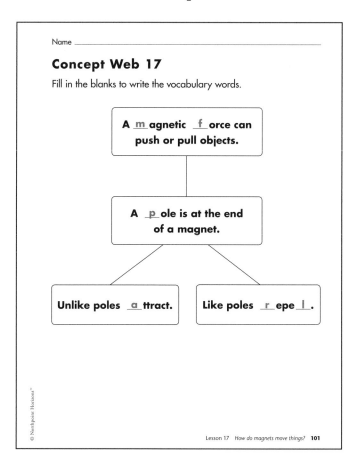

Name _____

Concept Web 17

Fill in the blanks to write the vocabulary words.

A _m_ agnetic _f_ orce can
push or pull objects.

A _p_ ole is at the end
of a magnet.

Unlike poles _a_ ttract.

Like poles _r_ epe _l_ .

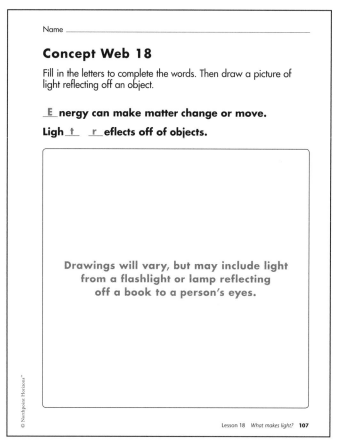

Name _____

Concept Web 18

Fill in the letters to complete the words. Then draw a picture of light reflecting off an object.

_E_ nergy can make matter change or move.

Ligh _t_ _r_ eflects off of objects.

Drawings will vary, but may include light from a flashlight or lamp reflecting off a book to a person's eyes.

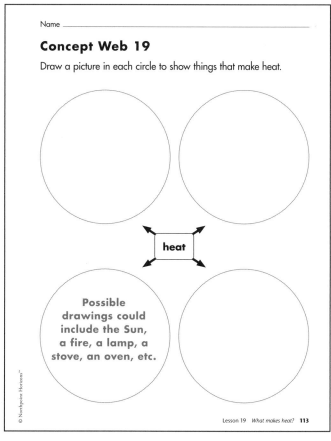

Name _____

Concept Web 19

Draw a picture in each circle to show things that make heat.

heat

Possible drawings could include the Sun, a fire, a lamp, a stove, an oven, etc.

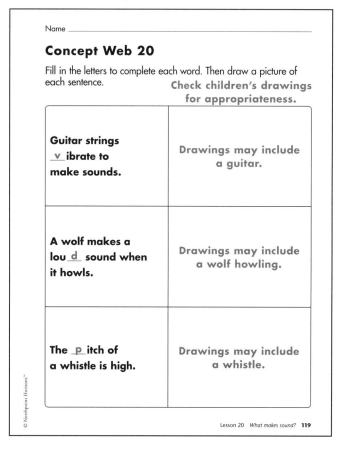

Name _____

Concept Web 20

Fill in the letters to complete each word. Then draw a picture of each sentence.

Check children's drawings for appropriateness.

Guitar strings _v_ ibrate to make sounds.	*Drawings may include a guitar.*
A wolf makes a lou _d_ sound when it howls.	*Drawings may include a wolf howling.*
The _p_ itch of a whistle is high.	*Drawings may include a whistle.*

Concept Web Answer Key Lessons 21–24

Concept Web 21

Fill in the letters to complete each word. Then draw a picture of each vocabulary word.

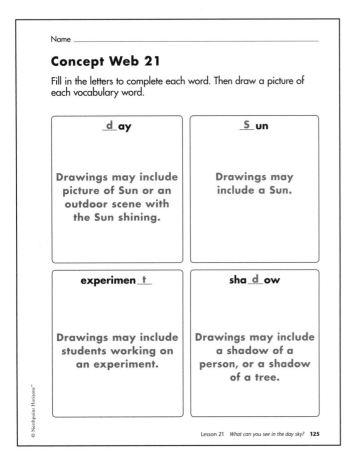

d ay

Drawings may include picture of Sun or an outdoor scene with the Sun shining.

S un

Drawings may include a Sun.

experimen t

Drawings may include students working on an experiment.

sha d ow

Drawings may include a shadow of a person, or a shadow of a tree.

Concept Web 22

Fill in the letters to complete each word. Then draw a picture of each word.

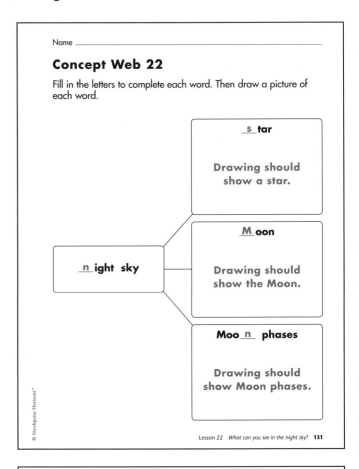

s tar

Drawing should show a star.

n ight sky

M oon

Drawing should show the Moon.

Moo n phases

Drawing should show Moon phases.

Concept Web 23

Fill in the letters to complete each word. Then draw a picture of each word.

a xis	Drawings may show Earth with its axis labeled.
r otation	Drawings may show Earth rotating on its axis.
o rbi t	Drawings may show Earth moving in its orbit around the Sun.

Concept Web 24

Fill in the letters to complete each word. Then draw a picture of each word.

p lane t

Drawing should show one of the planets in the solar system.

s olar s ystem

Drawing should show solar system.

s cientific m ethods

Drawing should show scientist using the scientific method.

Lesson Review Answer Key Lessons 1–4

Name _____

Lesson Review 1

Write the word from the box that completes each sentence.

plant	Living things	rock	Nonliving things

1. __Living things__ grow and change.

2. __Nonliving things__ do not grow and change.

3. A __plant__ is a living thing.

4. A __rock__ is a nonliving thing.

Name _____

Lesson Review 2

Write the word from the box that completes each sentence.

flower	leaf	life cycle	root	stem	seed

1. A __flower__ makes seeds.

2. A __root__ takes in water for a plant.

3. A __leaf__ makes food for a plant.

4. A __stem__ moves water up a plant.

5. Most plants grow from a __seed__ .

6. A plant grows and changes during its __life cycle__ .

Name _____

Lesson Review 3

Circle the names of the animals that have a backbone.

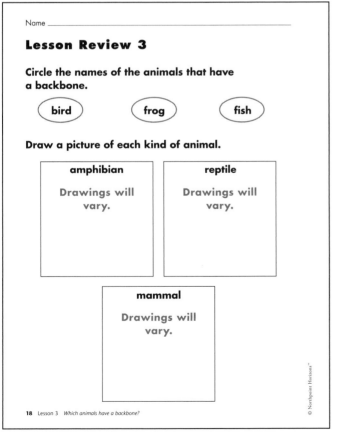

(bird)   (frog)   (fish)

Draw a picture of each kind of animal.

amphibian	reptile
Drawings will vary.	Drawings will vary.

mammal
Drawings will vary.

Name _____

Lesson Review 4

Draw pictures in the circles to show how a frog grows and changes.

Label each picture with a word from the box.

egg
tadpole

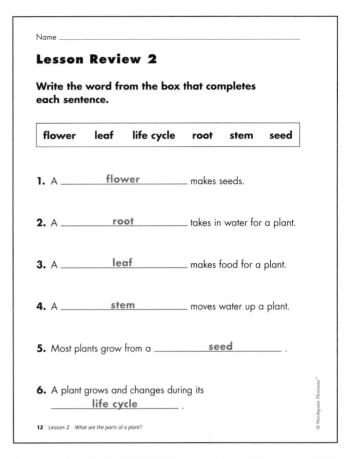

1. __egg__

3. __grown frog__

2. __tadpole__

Write words to complete the sentence.

4. The way a frog grows and changes is called a __life cycle__ .

Lesson Review Answer Key Lessons 5–8

Name

Lesson Review 5

Write the word from the box that completes
each sentence.

pupa	larva	life cycle

1. A butterfly grows and changes in a
_____ **life cycle** _____ .

2. A caterpillar is a butterfly _____ **larva** _____ .

3. A caterpillar changes to a _____ **pupa** _____ .

Lesson Review 6

Write a word from the box that completes
each sentence.

First	Next	life cycle	Last

1. _____ **Last** _____ the bunny becomes
a grown rabbit.

2. _____ **Next** _____ the bunny can find
its own food.

3. _____ **First** _____ a bunny drinks milk
from its mother.

4. A rabbit grows and changes during
its _____ **life cycle** _____ .

Lesson Review 7

Circle the word to complete each sentence.

1. The wings of a bat are _____ .
(**an adaptation**)   **a habitat**

2. A raccoon finds _____ in a tree.
camouflage   (**shelter**)

3. The place where an animal lives is its _____ .
camouflage   (**habitat**)

4. A forest is one kind of _____ .
adaptation   (**environment**)

5. An insect uses _____ to hide on a leaf.
an environment   (**camouflage**)

Lesson Review 8

Circle the word that completes each sentence.

1. Living things get energy from _____ .
predators   (**food**)

2. A frog eats an insect. The frog
is a _____ .
(**predator**)   **prey**

3. A turtle eats a plant. The plant
is a _____ .
consumer   (**producer**)

4. All the food chains in a swamp make up
a _____ .
producer   (**food web**)

Lesson Review Answer Key Lessons 9–12

Name _____

Lesson Review 9

Write the word from the box that completes each sentence.

condensation	evaporation	natural resource
precipitation	clouds	water cycle

1. Water is a __natural resource__ .

2. Water vapor changes to water drops during __condensation__ .

3. Water changes to a gas during __evaporation__ .

4. Rain, snow, and hail are kinds of __precipitation__ .

5. Water moves in the __water cycle__ .

6. Water drops in the sky form __clouds__ .

54   Lesson 9   *What is the water cycle?*

Name _____

Lesson Review 10

Draw a picture to show the weather today where you live.

> Drawings will vary.

Circle the word in each sentence that tells about the weather in the picture.   Answers will vary.

1. The weather is _____ .
   cold   hot

2. The weather is _____ .
   dry   wet

3. The weather is _____ .
   windy   not windy

60   Lesson 10   *What are some kinds of weather?*

Name _____

Lesson Review 11

Read each sentence about how Earth's land changes.

Circle the word to tell if the change is erosion, pollution, or weathering.

1. The roots of a tree cause a rock to break apart.
   erosion   pollution   (weathering)

2. Water moves pieces of rock.
   (erosion)   pollution   weathering

3. A lot of trash covers a beach.
   erosion   (pollution)   weathering

66   Lesson 11   *How does Earth's land change?*

Name _____

Lesson Review 12

Write the word from the box that completes each sentence.

season	temperature	thermometer

1. The __temperature__ is how hot or cold it is outside.

2. Weather changes with each new __season__ .

3. You measure temperature with a __thermometer__ .

Draw a picture of one season where you live. Write the name of the season below your picture.

> Pictures will vary.

72   Lesson 12   *What are seasons?*

Lesson Review Answer Key   **153**

Lesson Review Answer Key Lessons 13–16

Name

Lesson Review 13

Circle the answer to each question.

1. What is a dinosaur?

an animal that lives with scientists

(an animal that lived on Earth long ago)

2. What is a fossil?

(a footprint of an animal that lived long ago)

the name of a dinosaur

Draw a picture to show what scientists investigate.

Pictures will vary.

78 Lesson 13 *How do we learn about dinosaurs?*

© Northpoint Horizons™

Name

Lesson Review 14

Write the word from the box that completes each sentence.

balance	mass	matter

1. All _____ matter _____ takes up space.

2. All matter has _____ mass _____ .

3. You can measure mass with a _____ balance _____ .

Draw a picture of something that is matter.

Pictures will vary.

84 Lesson 14 *What is matter?*

© Northpoint Horizons™

Name

Lesson Review 15

Circle the answer for each question.

1. Which is a solid?

(rock)   water

2. Which is a liquid?

air   (water)

3. Which is a gas?

(air)   fish

4. Which is a mixture?

(gravel)   water

90 Lesson 15 *What forms does matter take?*

© Northpoint Horizons™

Name

Lesson Review 16

Write the word from the box that completes each sentence.

force	friction	motion	gravity

1. A force that pulls things to Earth is _____ gravity _____ .

2. A push or a pull is a _____ force _____ .

3. A force that makes moving things slow down is _____ friction _____ .

4. You use force to put an object in _____ motion _____ .

96 Lesson 16 *How do things move?*

© Northpoint Horizons™

Lesson Review Answer Key Lessons 17–20

Name _____

Lesson Review 17

The picture shows a bar magnet.

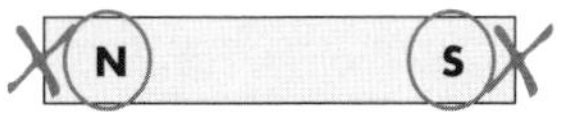

1. Circle the magnet's poles.

2. Put an X on the magnet where magnetic force is strongest.

Circle the word that completes each sentence.

3. Unlike poles of two magnets _____ each other.
(attract)   **repel**

4. Like poles of two magnets _____ each other.
attract   (repel)

Name _____

Lesson Review 18

Write the word from the box that completes each sentence.

Energy	Light	reflects

1. _____**Energy**_____ can make matter change or move.

2. Light from the flashlight _____**reflects**_____ from the book to the girl's eye.

3. _____**Light**_____ is energy we can see.

Draw something that makes light.

Drawings will vary.

Name _____

Lesson Review 19

Circle the sentences that are TRUE about heat. Put a line through the sentence that is NOT true about heat.

1. Heat is a kind of matter.

2. (A fire gives off heat.)

3. (Heat makes an object change temperature.)

Draw two things that make heat.

Drawings will vary.

Name _____

Lesson Review 20

Write the word from the box that completes each sentence.

loudness	pitch	vibrates

1. The _____**loudness**_____ of a sound is how loud or soft it is.

2. A sound is made when something _____**vibrates**_____ .

3. A drum has a low _____**pitch**_____ .

Draw something that makes sound.

Drawings will vary.

Lesson Review Answer Key Lessons 21–24

Name _____

Lesson Review 21

Write the word from the box that completes each sentence.

day	experiment	Sun	shadow

1. The _____Sun_____ gives light to Earth.

2. You see the Sun during the _____day_____ .

3. A _____shadow_____ is a dark shape made when something blocks light.

4. You can do an _____experiment_____ to learn about light.

Name _____

Lesson Review 22

Circle the word that completes each sentence.

1. _____ is when your part of Earth faces away from the Sun.
(Night)   Day

2. _____ reflects light from the Sun.
(The Moon)   A star

3. _____ is a hot ball of gas.
The Moon   (A star)

Draw pictures to show how the Moon phases change.

	Drawings should show Moon phases in correct order.	

Name _____

Lesson Review 23

Write the words from the box that completes each sentence.

axis	orbit	rotation	Sun

1. Earth spins on its _____axis_____ .

2. One whole spin is called a _____rotation_____ .

3. Earth moves around the _____Sun_____ .

4. The path Earth takes is called an _____orbit_____ .

Name _____

Lesson Review 24

Circle the word that completes each sentence.

1. Earth is a _____ .
star   (planet)

2. There are _____ planets in our solar system.
(eight)   ten

3. The planets in our solar system travel around the _____ .
(Sun)   Moon

Draw a picture.

Show a scientist using scientific methods to answer a question about the solar system.

Drawings will vary.
